Just in time for June...
Janet Dailey's <u>The Hostage Bride</u>

It's been said that Janet Dailey "wrote the book" on romance. And Silhouette Books is thrilled to announce that Janet Dailey, America's best-loved romance author, will now be writing for Silhouette Romances, starting with *The Hostage Bride* in June.

You may have enjoyed one of Janet's recent novels: *Touch the Wind*, *The Rogue* or *Ride the Thunder*. All three made *The New York Times* best-seller list—and together sold well over three million copies! Her latest book, *Night Way*, is currently on the best-seller list, and is another million-seller.

More than eighty million people have already fallen in love with Janet Dailey. Her books have been translated into seventeen languages and are now sold in *ninety* different countries around the world.

We're sure that you too, will fall in love with Janet Dailey's romance novels. Be sure to watch for *The Hostage Bride* this June.

W0010618

Dear Reader:

Silhouette Romances is an exciting new publishing venture. We will be presenting the very finest writers of contemporary romantic fiction as well as outstanding new talent in this field. It is our hope that our stories, our heroes and our heroines will give you, the reader, all you want from romantic fiction.

Also, *you* play an important part in our future plans for Silhouette Romances. We welcome any suggestions or comments on our books and I invite you to write to us at the address below.

So, enjoy this book and all the wonderful romances from Silhouette. They're for *you!*

Karen Solem
Editor-in-Chief
Silhouette Books
P.O. Box 769
New York, N.Y. 10019

PHYLLIS HALLDORSON
To Start Again

Silhouette Romance

Published by Silhouette Books New York

America's Publisher of Contemporary Romance

Other Silhouette Romances by Phyllis Halldorson

Temporary Bride

SILHOUETTE BOOKS, a Simon & Schuster Division of
GULF & WESTERN CORPORATION
1230 Avenue of the Americas, New York, N.Y. 10020

Copyright © 1981 by Phyllis Halldorson
Map copyright © 1981 by Tony Ferrara

Distributed by Pocket Books

ISBN: 0-671-57079-X

First Silhouette printing May, 1981

10 9 8 7 6 5 4 3 2 1

America's Publisher of Contemporary Romance

Printed in the U.S.A.

To Start Again

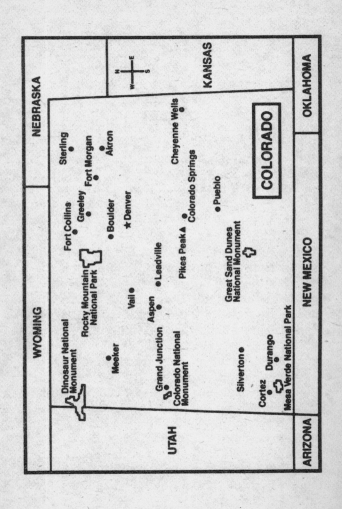

NEBRASKA

KANSAS

WYOMING

NEW MEXICO

OKLAHOMA

UTAH

ARIZONA

COLORADO

Sterling
Fort Collins
Greeley
Fort Morgan
Akron
Boulder
★ Denver
Cheyenne Wells
Colorado Springs
Pueblo
Pikes Peak ▲
Rocky Mountain National Park
Leadville
Great Sand Dunes National Monument
Vail
Aspen
Dinosaur National Monument
Meeker
Grand Junction
Colorado National Monument
Silverton
Durango
Cortez
Mesa Verde National Park

Chapter One

Anne pounded on the hood of her battered 1970 Ford as tears of frustration streamed down her face.

Traffic whizzed by on the highway, but no one paid any attention to the small blonde girl dressed in blue jeans, a navy windbreaker and bandana headscarf, shivering beside the stalled car until, finally, a red Grand Prix pulled to the side of the freeway behind her and a man and woman got out.

Anne watched warily as they approached her. They were young, early twenties, and well dressed, but they appeared to be quarreling. The man was of average height with brown hair and hazel eyes, and the woman could be described in the same adjectives as Anne herself. Five foot two, slender, blonde, brown eyes. They looked respectable, though, a lot more respectable than she did with her broken-down car and faded jeans.

She wiped the tears from her eyes with the back of one cold hand as the man said, "Need some help?"

He smiled and sounded cheerful, and some of Anne's fear of strangers subsided as she nodded. "I think my car just gave up and died. It refuses to go any further, and even if it could be fixed, I don't have any money."

The tears came again and she sniffled as the young woman put an arm around her and said, "Hey, you're freezing! Let's go sit in our car while Rory takes a look at yours." She shot a swift glance at her husband. "He never could resist a pretty girl who looked like she needed help."

Her husband glared back. "I keep hoping to find one with a little warmth and compassion."

He turned his back and bent over the car's motor. The woman stuck her tongue out at him in a childish gesture and led Anne back to the Grand Prix. It was new and warm, and Anne felt numb with cold. The November wind outside of Council Bluffs, Iowa had a freezing bite, and her jacket was lightweight.

The blonde woman settled herself beside Anne in the back seat and said, "I'm Angela Hawthorne. My husband and I are going to Denver to spend Thanksgiving with his folks." She grimaced. "I can think of a lot of things I'd rather do, but Rory insists that after a year of marriage it's time I met my in-laws."

Anne smiled. "My name's Anne Greenfield and I'm on my way to—uh—California. That is, I am if your husband can stick my car back together for long enough to make the trip."

Anne leaned back against the soft upholstery and

8

sighed. If the car was beyond repair she was stranded, with little money, no place to go and no one to turn to. When she'd left Chicago her only thought had been to put as much distance as she could between herself and Great Aunt Martha. She shuddered at the thought of Aunt Martha, with her slight body and whining voice that concealed a will of iron.

Anne could still hear her last threat, delivered in a tone that was anything but ladylike. "You walk out on me, you little ingrate, and I'll report your car stolen! It's registered in my name, don't forget, and I'll tell the police you stole it and ran away!"

That had been the last straw. The car was Anne's, bought with money she made babysitting and cleaning other people's houses, but she'd made the mistake of letting Aunt Martha talk her into registering it in her name for insurance purposes. Anne had no proof that the car belonged to her.

She'd slammed out of the house and driven west without a thought to where she was going until the car broke down and refused to budge another inch. Now she was really in trouble!

Anne was trying to focus her attention on Angela's conversation when Rory opened the door and climbed into the front seat, his face grim. Anne's heart sank even before he spoke. "Your transmission's shot. It will cost several hundred dollars to put another one in, and, frankly, the car's not worth it."

Anne slumped against the seat, a picture of total defeat. What was she going to do? She couldn't sit out there by the side of the road forever. She had no doubt that Aunt Martha would carry out her threat to report the car stolen. If the highway patrol came along and found her there, they'd arrest her and take her back.

No way was she going back there to be her aunt's personal slave! On the other hand, she had no training to qualify her to hold down a decent job. After graduating from high school two years ago, she had pleaded with her aunt to lend her the money to go on to college, but Aunt Martha had developed a sudden and mysterious ailment that left her a self-proclaimed invalid. Anne, mired in the quicksand of guilt and gratitude, had put aside her desire for a life of her own and stayed home to be nurse-companion-housekeeper for the tyrannical old lady.

A large hand on Anne's knee jerked her out of her reverie, and she looked up into Rory's appreciative eyes. He'd twisted around in the front seat to face her, as his hand lingered where it should never have been. "Don't look so down, gorgeous; we'll take you into Council Bluffs and you can call your family."

Anne shook her head and moved her leg to dislodge his probing hand. "I don't have a family. There's nothing for me to go back to in Chicago. That's why I was heading for California. Everyone knows there are lots of jobs out there. It's warm all the time and I can pick fruit, or work in a factory, or—"

"Don't count on it!" Rory's impatient voice cut off her recitation. "Unemployment is as rampant in California as it is here."

From Angela's side of the car came a short, nasty laugh. "Ha! What would you know about employ-

10

ment in California, or anywhere else for that matter? You've never in your life had to work!"

"What are you complaining about, my true and loving wife? You've never had it so good." Rory's voice was bitter.

Their bickering made Anne nervous and she tried to get the conversation back on the subject. "But everyone goes to California when they're looking for work!"

Rory nodded. "Sure. And what do you think they do with all those people who migrate there each year? Don't count on getting an unskilled job out there."

It was Rory who came up with a solution to her problem. "Look, we'll take you to Denver with us, if it will help. My family is in the mining business. Maybe they have an opening somewhere that you could qualify for."

Hope stirred in Anne. "You mean your father's a miner?"

Rory grinned. "Well, not in the sense you mean. He doesn't go out and pan for gold. He owns uranium mines. Come on, Anne, I'll help you get your stuff. We might as well leave the car by the side of the road. The highway patrol will have it junked eventually."

Angela sat in the back seat with Anne, and in answer to Anne's query about where they were from, Angela answered, "We live in Cambridge, Massachusetts. Rory's a senior at Harvard and I'm a freshman at Radcliffe." She giggled. "I was a waitress when I married Rory, but that wasn't good enough for his parents and his older brother,

11

Matthew, so they insisted on sending me to college too." Angela wrinkled her nose distastefully. "Radcliffe's a snooty school. The only thing that got me in is the fact that my husband's a Hawthorne, of *the* Colorado Hawthornes, and a student at Harvard."

Rory snorted. "That's also what got you into my bed, so don't knock it. Believe me, if you pick up a little class along the way, it can only be an improvement."

Angela roared with indignation and answered him in kind, and as Anne watched them she realized that they were a rather mismatched pair. Angela's blonde hair was bleached rather than natural, and she wore too much of the wrong kind of makeup. Her face had a hard look of sophistication that made her seem older than the twenty-four years she claimed.

Rory, two years younger than Angela, had the easy hauteur that money and education breed, but he seemed bitter and antagonistic. Anne began to wonder if she had been wise to agree to ride all the way to Denver with them. When she and Rory had gone to get her bags from her car, he'd managed to brush up against her in a suggestive way and that, combined with the way he and Angela were going at it, made her wonder just *why* he was being so nice to her.

The car sped down highway 80 past Council Bluffs, across the Missouri river and into Omaha, Nebraska, then south to Lincoln. On the outskirts of Lincoln they stopped at a roadside café for lunch and afterwards turned south and headed across the vast prairie that was Nebraska. Rory and Angela had been sniping at each other all the way, and Anne wondered how they'd ever make it to Denver. It was in the late afternoon, just a few miles east of North Platt, that things suddenly changed.

It was cold and windy and the snow that had been hovering overhead in thick, moist clouds fell like small white feathers against the windshield. Angela was sitting in the front seat but had twisted around so she could face Anne. They had been discussing the rash on Angela's fingers, caused by a new detergent she had been using, and she was rummaging through her purse and grumbling, "Now where did I put that? Oh, here it is—"

She handed a small Tiffany jeweler's case to Anne. "Open it; I want you to see my rings. I can't wear them right now because of the rash."

Anne opened the box and gasped. The brilliance of the diamond engagement ring was breathtaking. She lifted the rings out of their blue velvet setting and Angela said, "Look inside the band. We had our initials and the date of our marriage engraved there." While Anne examined the engraving in the glowing gold, Angela continued talking. "Put them on your finger—that's right, third finger, left hand. They fit like they'd been sized for you. Have you noticed how much alike we look? With those rings on, you're just like me. She lifted her expensive leather purse and handed it to Anne. "Here, put my purse back there. It's in the way up here."

Anne took the purse and settled back. It was then that she saw the other car. It had skidded on the slick road, made a 380 degree turn and now was headed right for them! She screamed as Rory swerved to avoid the other car, but he was too late. The wrenching jolt of the impact brought the terrible crunching sound of metal tearing into metal, hot burning pain, and darkness as she drifted down, down, down. . . .

It was the pain that edged Anne back to awareness. It throbbed through her head and right arm and settled into an ache throughout her chest. It hurt to breathe and her arms were restricted in some way. She couldn't move them. She rolled her head to one side and agony exploded inside her skull. She cried out and felt a hand on her shoulder. She knew she should open her eyes, but they were weighted down. A cool, professional-sounding voice above her gave orders.

"Lie still, Angela, and it won't hurt so much. Can you open your eyes and look at me?"

Angela? The voice was talking to Angela. Was Angela all right? Anne tried to move again and moaned as the torment returned, but only for a moment. She sighed as the welcome blackness engulfed her.

It was voices that woke her the second time. The high-pitched voice of a woman and the deep baritone of a man. The woman seemed to be reassuring the man as Anne listened.

"I know she looks pretty bad, Mr. Hawthorne, but, actually, she was very lucky. For awhile we thought she might have internal injuries, but all the tests were negative. She was thrown out of the car and escaped with a fractured arm, two broken ribs

14

and a concussion. It's the head injury that caused those black eyes, but she should be able to travel in a few days."

Anne moved her head. It hurt, but not with the shattering anguish she had felt before. Her arms still wouldn't move, but her legs were free. If the man and woman were talking about her, then no wonder she hurt all over. She wondered where she was. If she could only open her eyes.

The woman had called the man "Mr. Hawthorne." Rory? Of course, it had to be Rory. He sounded all right, so he must not have been badly hurt. She breathed a sigh of relief and murmured, "Rory."

She tried again to open her eyes, but all she could see were little slits of light. A large hand touched her left arm and the rich baritone voice said, "I'm Matt, Angela. Matthew Hawthorne, Rory's brother."

Again she tried to open her eyes but couldn't. She shifted restlessly and groaned as pain shot off in all directions.

"I can't see you. Where is Rory? Was he hurt badly?"

The hand tightened on her arm and the voice said, "Your eyes are swollen shut. It's nothing to worry about, but you'd better prepare yourself for bad news." He seemed to choke but continued. "Rory and your other passenger were killed in the crash."

She stiffened and cried out with the pain her sudden movement caused. Dead! Both Rory and Angela were dead! Those two people, so vitally alive, the only people to take an interest in her, were dead. What a waste; what a dreadful, awful waste!

She whimpered softly as tears slid out from beneath her closed eyelids and the woman spoke from the other side of the bed. "Go ahead and cry, Angela. I'll be back in a few minutes with something to relax you."

Angela? Why were they calling her Angela? Maybe she had just misunderstood. She hurt too much and was too confused to try to think, and she made no attempt to control the tears of grief that slid down her cheeks onto the pillow. The man with the baritone voice and the gentle touch sat beside her with her hand in his until she drifted off to sleep.

When Anne woke for the third time she was able to open her eyes, but the brightness of the sun streaming in her window hurt them. She hurt all over, so it really didn't matter. At least she could see again. Not that there was much to see, she thought. The room she was in was decorated in shades of light green, but it was still a hospital room.

She turned her head and saw that her right arm was encased in a heavy cast. What a mess she must be! Somewhere long ago she remembered a nurse saying she was lucky to be alive, but now she wondered. What was going to become of her?

She didn't know how long she'd been in the hospital, but there was certainly no way she could pay for it. Had they discovered who she was and notified her aunt? Anne shuddered as she remembered Aunt Martha's pathetic speech, delivered every time Anne wanted a little independence.

She'd dab at her eyes with a handkerchief as she whined, "How could you go against my wishes? After all I've done for you! Why, you were a penniless orphan when I took you in. I gave you a home, fed you, bought your clothes, and this is the way you repay me."

It worked every time, and Anne found herself sinking deeper into bondage as she gradually gave up her normal schoolgirl desires and most of her friends to be the selfish woman's unpaid servant. Now she'd finally gotten the nerve to break away, and nobody could make her go back. She'd do anything to stay as far away from Aunt Martha as possible!

The door opened and a dark-haired nurse came in. She saw that Anne was awake and smiled. "Good morning, Angela. How are you feeling?"

Anne frowned and said, "My name's Anne."

The nurse stuck a thermometer in Anne's mouth and felt for her pulse as she answered, "Oh, they call you Anne? I guess it's easier to say than Angela. You're looking better this morning; are you having much pain?"

Anne couldn't correct her about the name with her mouth full of thermometer, so she just shook her head in answer to the question. The nurse made a notation on her chart and said, "That handsome brother-in-law of yours left word he'd be back around eleven." She shook her head admiringly. "He is the nicest man I ever met. He came from Denver as soon as we notified him that you were here, and he's been haunting the hospital for days."

The nurse took the thermometer out of her mouth and Anne said, "Brother-in-law?" She was beginning to wonder if the woman had lost her mind. What on earth was she talking about?

The nurse read the thermometer. "Matthew Hawthorne," she answered. "Don't you remember talking to him last night? I certainly wish I had a brother-in-law like him. He's assumed responsibility for all your medical expenses, and as soon as you're well enough to be moved, he's taking you by ambulance back to his family in Denver."

She shook down the thermometer, made another notation on her chart and then turned to leave. "You're doing just fine, Anne. I'll send Mr. Hawthorne in as soon as he comes."

Anne was too shocked to speak. Why would the Hawthornes pay her medical expenses and take her to Denver to live with them? They'd never even heard of her until they found out that she was the only survivor in the accident that killed their son and daughter-in-law. The last word triggered a memory. What was it the nurse had called Mr. Hawthorne? Her brother-in-law? But he was *Angela's* brother-in-law, not hers.

A cold chill crept up her spine. Everyone here at the hospital had been calling her "Angela," even Matthew Hawthorne. Was it possible that they thought—? No, of course not. There was no way they could have mistaken her for Angela Hawthorne! Why, they didn't even look that much alike. And even if the hospital personnel had made a mistake, Matthew Hawthorne would certainly have known the difference.

Or would he? What was it Angela had said about her husband's family? Anne tried to remember, but the events of that whole day of the accident were

18

muddled in her mind. Her head was beginning to throb again and she gave up and dozed.

A footstep by the bed roused her. She opened her eyes and looked directly into a pair of dark ones, as deep a brown as the color of chocolate. She blinked, and the man attached to the eyes straightened and said, "I'm sorry if I disturbed you; I didn't realize you were sleeping."

She would know that voice anywhere. It was the deep, rich baritone that had drifted to her through the fog of her unconsciousness. The voice that told her that Rory Hawthorne was dead. She hadn't been able to see him then, but now he was too close to miss. He towered above the bed, but she suspected he wouldn't seem quite so tall if she were standing beside him instead of lying nearly at his feet. He was wearing a brown and beige wool tweed overcoat with a sheer, gold wool scarf at the throat. His dark head was uncovered. He had a broad forehead and a strong jaw that jutted out at a stubborn angle. He had the bearing of a man who knows what he wants and gets it, and he was much older than Rory's twenty-two years.

She must have hesitated too long because he frowned and said, "Don't you remember me? I'm Matthew Hawthorne, Rory's brother."

She moistened her lips and replied. "Yes, of course, I was just confused for a moment. Won't you sit down?"

He removed his coat and hung it over the back of the chair, then sat down facing the bed. He was long and lean, and his brown business suit was impecca-

19

bly tailored. He studied her for a minute, then said, "You're looking better today. At least you can open your eyes. Do you feel up to answering a few questions? The police are anxious to verify the identity of your passenger."

"My—my passenger?" Anne stammered.

"The person riding in the car with you and Rory. A purse was found at the scene with a driver's license made out to a Martha Greenfield. Was that her name? Martha Anne Greenfield?"

Somehow, hearing him talk about her this way, as if she wasn't here—or anywhere!—was worse than anything that had gone before. She turned her head into the pillow and sobbed.

Matthew murmured an awkward apology and stood. Anne struggled to bring her emotions under control. Would the shock and horror never go away?

She'd wished she could reach out and touch Matthew when he leaned over her to say goodbye. He was so big and strong and utterly male, but the anguish in his dark eyes told her how deeply he felt the death of his young brother.

Did he have a wife to comfort him when he got back to Denver? She knew nothing about Rory's family—and, yet they thought she was Angela. She remembered now that Angela had said she was going to meet her in-laws for the first time. They didn't know Angela, and Angela's description did fit Anne. But they'd found Anne's purse.

She made a face as she remembered Matthew saying the driver's license was in the name of Martha Greenfield. She'd been named Martha Anne after her Aunt Martha, her only living relative, but she'd always been called Anne. Why did they think the purse belonged to the woman who had been killed?

The nurse came in with a lunch tray and interrupted Anne's musing. She set the tray on the bedside table and raised the bed to a sitting position; for a minute Anne felt dizzy, but soon the whirling in her head was gone. She lifted the cover of the largest dish and peeked underneath. It was a fluffy yellow omelette garnished with sprigs of green parsley. She realized she was hungry. She hadn't eaten since lunch the day of the accident. How long ago was that? All she could remember was drifting in and out of consciousness.

The nurse poured hot chocolate, steamy and fragrant, from the heavy china pot as Anne asked, "How long have I been here?"

The nurse removed the cover from a plate of hot muffins and said, "Let's see, you were brought in Monday evening and this is Thursday—Thanksgiving. That's three days."

Three days! But it couldn't have been that long. Yet the nurse had said today was Thanksgiving. Rory and Angela had been on their way to Denver to spend Thanksgiving with his family. They hadn't even lived long enough for Angela to meet her in-laws. Instead, Matthew was spending Thanksgiving alone in a small city on the Nebraska prairie while he arranged to ship Rory's body home. Poor Matthew. He was in for yet another shock. When he came back she'd have to tell him that Angela had died in the accident, too. She couldn't let him go on thinking that she, Anne, was his sister-in-law.

She enjoyed the light meal, although trying to eat

21

with her left hand was slow and awkward. When the nurse came back, Anne asked for a mirror. The nurse showed her how to raise the looking glass on the over-the-bed table.

Anne gasped when she saw herself. She looked like the monster in a horror movie. Both eyes were black and puffy, there was a purple bruise on her forehead and her hair hung in limp strands to her shoulders.

She whimpered softly, and the nurse turned to look at her. "Don't be upset; the bruises are already fading. Before long you'll look as good as new." She turned toward the door. "I'll get your purse. You've probably got some makeup in it, and a little lipstick would help."

She left and returned almost immediately with an expensive leather purse. Angela's purse! The one she'd given to Anne just before the crash.

Anne moistened her lips and said, "Where did you get this purse?"

The nurse picked up the tray containing the empty lunch dishes. "You were clutching it to you when they brought you in. That's how we found out who you were, from the license and other identification in there. And, of course, your rings.

Anne blinked. "Rings?"

The nurse nodded. "Your engagement and wedding rings. They looked very valuable, so we took them off your finger and put them, and your purse, in the safe until you regained consciousness. You'll find them inside the purse. Now put on some lipstick, and tomorrow, if you feel up to it, I'll wash your hair."

She left, but Anne hardly heard the last sentence. She opened the purse and took out the rings. *Angela*'s rings. Anne had tried them on just before the accident, and now she realized that everything had happened so quickly that she'd never had a chance to take them off. No wonder everyone thought she was Angela! When Matthew came she would tell him the truth.

But what would happen to *her?* The family would withdraw all support once Matthew found out she wasn't related to them. He had no obligation to a stranger, a runaway girl who had taken a ride with his brother and sister-in-law and just happened to be in their car when it crashed. He'd turn her over to the authorities and go back to Denver, and she'd be sent back to Chicago to face a charge of car theft.

Anne knew it was really emotional blackmail. Aunt Martha would be glad to drop the charge if Anne would agree to stay with her and marry Clarence Brewer. Anne shuddered. Clarence was the son of Aunt Martha's best friend, and it had long been the two women's dream to see Anne married to him. But she had to grow up first, and while she was accomplishing this, Mrs. Brewer had died. After that, Aunt Martha felt doubly dedicated to the cause of carrying out her friend's wish.

Clarence, eight years older than Anne and already going bald, was used to doing as his mother told him, and he was content to wait for Anne. He took her to a movie every Saturday night and gave her a cool kiss on the cheek when he took her home. On Sunday mornings he escorted the two women to church. The rest of the week he stayed home and

23

went to bed early to conserve his strength for his job, a clerical position at the bank. Clarence wore rimless glasses and dark conservative suits; he was bossy, fastidious and dull.

Anne had no other boyfriends; Aunt Martha kept her too busy with housework, cooking and running errands to have any social life. Even so, she never took the idea of marrying Clarence seriously until last week, when he had presented her with a small diamond engagement ring on her twentieth birthday. She protested, insisting she was still too young, but for once Clarence was adamant. Since she didn't want to make a scene, she let him slip it on her finger. It wasn't until a few days later that Clarence and Aunt Martha together confronted Anne with their little bombshell. The wedding would take place within the month and the newlyweds would move into Aunt Martha's house and live with her. Anne, of course, would stay home and take care of the house, Aunt Martha and the children that would come along at suitably planned intervals while Clarence toiled at the bank to support them.

Anne rebelled! Living with Aunt Martha was bad enough; marriage to Clarence would probably be no better, and the two together were unthinkable! She gave Clarence back his ring and started to pack. Aunt Martha threatened, and Anne left in a towering rage. She'd never go back. Never! No matter what she had to do.

She took a deep breath and opened Angela's purse. There was a billfold with several bills in it, almost fifty dollars. There was also a bank credit card and a driver's license. It identified the smiling

24

blonde in the photo as Angela Langford Hawthorne, a resident of Cambridge, Massachusetts, age twenty-four years.

A plastic case filled with makeup, a comb, a package of chewing gum, a small mirror, several tissues and a ball point pen completed the inventory. Anne closed the purse and set it on the bedside table. There was nothing to reveal Angela Hawthorne's way of life or personality in the bag that was all that was left of her.

Dare she play out this little charade? Would it really be so wrong to take Angela's identity for a little while? Angela had no further use for it and Anne needed it desperately. What harm would it do to let the Hawthornes think she was their daughter-in-law? She'd be very careful not to do anything to hurt them, and she'd pay back every cent they spent on her just as soon as she was well enough to get a job. She'd be a daughter they could be proud of.

The sound of voices in the hall distracted her. Matthew appeared in the doorway with another man, shorter and not nearly as handsome or well dressed, beside him.

Matthew greeted her and said, "Angela, this is Officer Smith. He'd like to ask you some questions about the accident."

The policeman sat in the chair with a notebook and pen while Matthew stood with his back to them, looking out the window at the bare, gray trees. Anne watched the policeman apprehensively. Did she dare lie to him? Could they send her to jail if she did? They would almost certainly arrest her for car theft if she didn't.

He certainly seemed friendly enough. "For purposes of identification, ma'am, will you tell me your name and where you're from?"

Anne hesitated. What she said now could affect the whole course of her life. Did she have the nerve to pose as Rory Hawthorne's widow? What would happen to her if she told the policeman that Angela Hawthorne was the woman killed in the car accident?

For a moment her thoughts returned to Aunt Martha and Clarence in Chicago. If she went back there she might as well be in jail. Marriage to a man she didn't love, who wanted her only because she was his mother's choice, would be worse than prison. With Aunt Martha thrown in . . . ! She had no choice.

She clenched her fists and answered quickly, "My name is Angela Langford Hawthorne; I live in Cambridge, Massachusetts, and I'm a student at Radcliffe college."

The policeman nodded and asked his next question. "Who was the third person in the car with you and your husband?"

Anne took a deep breath and recited her own obituary. "Her name was Martha Greenfield and she said she was from Chicago. That's all I know about her."

26

Chapter Two

On Friday, the day after Thanksgiving, Matthew brought good news when he came to see Anne. He looked relieved as he said, "I just talked to your doctor and he says you're strong enough to travel to Denver by ambulance tomorrow. Do you feel up to it?"

So it was beginning, her new life. She would go to Denver and be a member of the Hawthorne family, a family with money and prestige. She would be the pampered daughter-in-law of a very wealthy man.

A stab of guilt pricked her, but she pushed it away. Why not? Angela was dead, but she, Anne, was very much alive and desperately in need of someone to care for her, protect her, love her.

She smiled up at Matthew. "Of course, but I don't want to go in an ambulance. Why can't I ride in the car with you?"

He frowned. "It's almost four hundred miles,

27

Angela. You'd be more comfortable in an ambulance."

"But traveling all that way by ambulance would cost a fortune!" she argued. "If you have a big car I can lie down in back when I get tired."

He looked surprised. "What's gotten into you? You never objected to spending money before."

Anne knew she'd made a mistake and quickly tried to cover it, but she couldn't suppress the anger his biting retort had roused. "How do you know how much money I spend?"

"I should," he grumbled, "I pay the bills, remember? I also make out a hefty monthly check that you and Rory manage to dispose of without difficulty."

Anne was stunned by his apparent disapproval of his brother and sister-in-law's spending habits. What had she gotten herself into? Up to now he'd been so concerned about her, so gentle.

She sighed. "I'm sorry, I didn't realize you were upset with us."

His eyes snapped with anger as he barked, "Oh, come off it, Angela! It was less than two weeks ago that I told both of you on the phone that I was going to close out your charge accounts if you didn't stop spending so much money. As I remember, you insisted that buying two mink coats wasn't an extravagance because one was short and the other long."

Anne was appalled. Had Angela really been so greedy? And now Anne was being blamed for it. She felt tears form and tried to blink them back. It was stupid to cry because Matthew was yelling at her. It

28

was really Angela he was mad at, but now she was Angela and for some reason it hurt unbearably to have him angry with her.

The tears welled in her brown eyes and spilled down her cheeks. Matthew looked at her and muttered, "Oh, blast! I'm sorry, don't cry."

He sat on the edge of the bed and took a handkerchief from the pocket of his snug-fitting slacks that revealed a flat stomach and slim, muscular thighs. His voice softened as he said, "Please, Angela, don't cry."

He dabbed at the tears with the white linen handkerchief. "I didn't mean to upset you. It's just that this has been one lousy week and my nerves are shot."

He handed her the handkerchief and wiped the tears away with his fingertips, sending little ripples of pleasure down her spine. She wondered again if he was married. She didn't dare ask him; that was one thing Angela would have known.

She reached out her left hand and cupped his cheek. It was smooth, with just a hint of the beard he'd shaved off earlier. She smiled a sad little smile as she said, "Poor Matthew, I've been so wrapped up in my own problems I forgot how you must be suffering." Her fingers caressed his face.

She sat up straight and leaned toward him as she stroked his hair. "Let me help."

His arms were around her, drawing her close against him as he murmured, "Oh, Angela," and buried his face in her left shoulder, but almost immediately he pushed her away with a muffled oath and jumped up. His voice was rough with anger as he turned away from her. "Don't try it, Angela, it won't work!"

Anne's first reaction was surprise. "Don't try what? I don't understand, I just—"

"I know what you're doing," he interrupted, "but you're not dealing with Rory now. You're not my type, so leave me alone!" He strode toward the door and was gone.

The next day, Saturday, was gray and overcast. When Matthew arrived at the hospital shortly after breakfast, his cheeks were red with cold. He was carrying several boxes bearing the name of a local dress shop. He put them on Anne's lap and shrugged out of his heavy overcoat as he said, "You need clothes to travel in; everything you had with you was destroyed in the fire. I hope these fit; they're not exactly designer quality but they'll do."

Not a word about the embarrassing scene yesterday. Anne couldn't control the flush she felt creeping over her, and she wouldn't look at him. Instead, she eyed the packages in her lap and cautiously picked one up.

Matthew jammed his hands in his pockets and muttered, "Can you open them or do you need help?"

Anne nodded, still unable to look at him or speak. She was beginning to use the fingers that projected from the heavy cast on her right hand, and she was able to undo the boxes by herself.

She gasped as she opened package after package. There were two pantsuits with gathered tops and flowing sleeves to accommodate her cast, shoes, a robe and nightie, and an oversized box that contained a hip-length fake fur cape. It was the most beautiful coat Anne had ever seen and for a moment she was speechless.

Matthew misunderstood and his voice was harsh. "Sorry it's not up to your usual standards. Since you already have two mink coats and a leather jacket, I didn't figure you needed another expensive one."

The hostility in his voice dimmed her appreciation, and she sat there running her fingers through the soft, sleek fur, murmuring simply, "Thank you."

The last box was filled with underwear and pantyhose. Before she realized what it was, she reached in and brought out a pair of bikini panties, a slim band of satin trimmed with wide strips of elasticized lace. Anne dropped it quickly and felt the familiar flush crawl up her neck and cheeks.

Matthew shifted impatiently. "Angela, I'm surprised at you. I didn't think you knew how to blush. I may not be married, but I'm thirty years old and I've known for a long time now what women wear under their dresses."

Anne was so relieved to hear he wasn't married that she forgot her discomfort and held up a tissue-sheer bra to read the size tag. She was astonished and said so. "How did you know my size?"

Matthew shrugged. "I asked the nurse to check the size of the underwear you were wearing when you were brought in. If you still want to ride in the car with me, get dressed. I'll be ready to start when you are."

He left the room in search of a nurse to help her.

31

Anne started the trip sitting with Matthew in the front seat of the luxurious Chrysler New Yorker, but after a couple of hours she was tired and ached all over, so Matthew insisted she lie down on the wide back seat. He'd brought a pillow and a blanket and she was warm and comfortable, but after a while the slight sway of the car made her queasy and she had to sit up again. By the time they got to Sterling, Colorado, she was exhausted. Matthew took one look at her and started looking for a motel.

"We'll stop for tonight and finish the trip tomorrow," he told her, and she didn't argue.

It was snowing heavily by this time, and apparently most of the other motorists had decided to pull off the road early, too. They tried several motels before Matthew came out of the office of the last one and said, "I hope you don't mind sharing a room with me. They only had one left, but it has two double beds."

He seemed to take her acceptance for granted and drove the sleek car up to number fifteen. Anne was shocked at the idea of spending the night in the same bedroom with a man. Never before had she been caught in a situation like this. Clarence had never gone further than holding her hand and kissing her on the cheek, but Matthew was no Clarence. He was thirty years old and admittedly experienced with women. What did he want of her? Surely he wouldn't expect . . . ?

She shuddered, and when Matthew opened the door to help her out, she shrank back. He looked at her curiously and muttered, "What's the matter,

32

isn't it fancy enough for you? Sorry, but beggars can't be choosers. It's the only motel room in town."

Now she'd made him angry again. She took his extended hand and let him guide her out of the car as she said, "No, it's not that. I guess I'm just tired."

The room was nice, nicer than any Anne had been in before. There was a green carpet on the floor, and the beds were covered with gold and brown quilted bedspreads. Matthew returned with their suitcases, helped her out of the fake fur cape and hung it in the closet along with his heavy overcoat. Anne collapsed on one of the beds, too tired to care about anything. She heard Matthew stirring around the room and was almost asleep when he sat down on the side of her bed and began removing her shoes. Her eyes flew open and she saw Matthew's startled expression as she jerked her feet up and curled them under her.

He sounded exasperated as he said, "Now what's wrong? You don't intend to sleep with your clothes on, do you?"

Her heart was pounding and not altogether with fear as she answered, "No, but I can undress myself!"

He raised one eyebrow. "How? The nurse dressed you this morning. With two broken ribs and a fractured arm, you're pretty restricted in what you can do."

He was right. Not only that, but her blouse buttoned down the back and there was no way she could get out of it without help. To make matters worse, she wasn't wearing a bra. The elastic bandage that had been wound around her ribs to protect the

33

broken ones had provided enough bulk to keep the bra from fastening comfortably, so she'd left it off. What was she going to do? She could hardly let a strange man undress her!

She wasn't given a choice as Matthew continued to remove her shoes and the knee-length nylons she wore with them. He put them neatly on the floor beside the bed and commanded, "Roll over a little so I can unbutton your blouse."

She gasped and continued to lie on her back as fear inched along her spine and branched throughout her body. She shook her head, and the fear was in her voice as she said, "No. Go away. I'd rather sleep in my clothes."

He looked at her for a moment as if he couldn't believe what was happening, then exploded with rage. "What on earth is the matter with you, Angela? You act like you'd been raised in a convent! You're hardly a sixteen-year-old virgin!"

No, Anne thought, *I'm a twenty-year-old virgin!*

Matthew continued his verbal lashing. "Just what do you think I'm going to do to you? You can't possibly think I'd rape you! I told you, your type doesn't appeal to me, even if you weren't my brother's wife!"

He got up and stalked into the bathroom, slamming the door behind him.

Anne felt thoroughly chastised. What *was* the matter with her? Matthew had never been anything but a gentleman. He'd paid her hospital bills, bought her clothes, let her slow his trip home by taking her with him instead of making her go in an ambulance, and she repaid him by suspecting him of being some

34

kind of monster who would take advantage of a nearly helpless girl, and his sister-in-law at that.

Oh, why had she ever gotten herself into this mess? Why hadn't she told him the truth? It was legally impossible for Aunt Martha to force her to marry Clarence, and she could have proved somehow that the car was hers and she hadn't stolen it. She was no longer a teenager; why did she have to be such a baby? Other girls her age left home. They usually moved in with some fellow and got along fine. Why couldn't she be like them? Why was she such a little puritan?

The shower that she had heard running in the bathroom was abruptly turned off, and a few minutes later Matthew emerged wearing nothing but a towel draped around his narrow hips. He was slim and muscular, with a mat of dark hair on his chest. His legs weren't bony like most men's but fleshed out like a runner's, and the muscles flexed as he walked across the room. She blushed and looked away as an unfamiliar warmth stirred in her.

He didn't even look at her as he began gathering up some clean clothes. She sat up painfully and asked, "Where are you going?"

He still didn't look at her as he started toward the bathroom again. "I'm going out for dinner. I'll bring you back something to eat and then go find another room—somewhere."

He went back in the bathroom and closed the door.

Anne sat there, shocked. Well, what had she expected? She'd insulted him beyond forgiveness, and he probably couldn't stand the sight of her. Why couldn't she ever do anything right? She'd botched up everything she'd ever tried to do and now she couldn't even start a new life without messing that up from the beginning, too. Well, this time she was going to try to make amends. For some reason, making Matthew like her was the most important thing in the world to her right now. She got off the bed and limped to the bathroom door and knocked.

Matthew's muffled voice answered. "I'll be out in a minute."

She called softly, "Matthew, I'm sorry."

The door opened and he almost ran into her. He'd changed into dark slacks and a heavy hand-knit sweater. His dark hair, touseled a few minutes ago, was now neatly combed, and he smelled of expensive after-shave lotion.

He looked down at her and said, "Did you want to use the bathroom?"

She shook her head. "No, I wanted to ask if you'd help me undress."

His brown eyes searched hers. "Aren't you afraid I'll lose control and ravish you?"

Her lips trembled but she didn't avert her gaze. "You'd never do that, even if you wanted me. I'm sorry I behaved like such a fool. I haven't been thinking very straight lately, but . . . but I want you to stay. I know you'd get along just fine without me, but you're right—I do need you."

She looked away then, ashamed of her vulnerability and of the feelings churning inside her. She wanted him to touch her, to take her in his arms and hold her, to keep her safe.

There was a catch in his voice as he said, "Where's your nightgown?"

"I'll get it." She opened her suitcase, another gift from him, took out the flowing ivory gown and handed it to him.

He laid it across the bed and said, "Turn around."

She did, and he unfastened her blouse, slipped it off and then helped her into her nightie, all the time facing her back.

"Do you need help getting out of your slacks?" he asked.

She couldn't control the embarrassed flush that sent waves of heat through her, but her voice was steady as she said, "Yes, please."

He turned her toward him, pulled up her nightgown and slid the slacks, which were loose fitting and had an elastic waist, down around her hips. He let them fall to the floor as the skirt of her nightgown once more dropped around her ankles. There was nothing sensuous or suggestive about it. He might as well have been undressing a child. She was oddly disappointed.

She put her hand on his shoulder and stood on tiptoe to brush her lips lightly across his as she said, "Thank you."

He stiffened, but smiled, and bent to pull back the covers on her bed. He helped her lie down, pulled the covers up around her chin and said, "When we get to Denver I promise you'll have a maid to help you."

She grinned up at him, suddenly brave. "I'd rather have you, Matthew."

He grinned back. "Don't press your luck, little girl, and why do you keep calling me Matthew?"

Her eyes widened. "But that's your name."

"Of course, but you never called me that before. In your letters and phone conversations you always called me Matt, like everyone else does. No one but my mother calls me Matthew, and you don't remind me a bit of my mother."

Anne squirmed. How many more mistakes like that was she going to make, and how long would it be before he began to be suspicious of them? On the other hand, this was a good opening to get her name straightened out, too. She couldn't stand to have him call her Angela. She bit her lip and said, "I'm sorry, but I was shy about talking to you face to face. Speaking of names, I wish you'd call me Anne."

"Anne?" He sounded dubious. "Why should I call you Anne?"

"I've always been known as Anne; it's short for Angela."

Matt frowned. "I never knew Rory to refer to you as anything but Angela."

Oh, darn, she'd forgotten about Rory. She paused a moment, then got her thoughts collected and said, "I know. He's the only one who called me Angela. He said it stood for Angel. It—it was sort of special between us."

The pain was back in Matt's eyes again, but so was a hint of disbelief, as he said, "And it hurts to have anyone else call you by Rory's special name? I'm sorry. After this you'll be Anne to me. Now, tell me what you want me to bring you for dinner."

She snuggled into the soft mattress and realized

38

she was so tired she could hardly keep her eyes open. "I don't want anything to eat; I'd rather sleep. You can buy me a big breakfast in the morning."

He got up, took his coat from the closet and was putting it on when she remembered something she had to make sure of. She opened her eyes and called, "Matt, you will come back and spend the night here, won't you?"

He nodded, and there was something she couldn't recognize in his eyes. "If you're sure that's what you want."

She closed her eyes again, content. "I'm sure."

She didn't wake the next morning, Sunday, until ten o'clock. When she asked Matt why he hadn't called her he said she needed her sleep. She went to the bathroom and found again how limited she was in her movements. She had to brush her teeth and wash her face with her left hand, and it was slow going and awkward. When she was finished, Matt was waiting to help her dress. She'd managed a change of panties in the bathroom, and Matt dressed her the same way he'd undressed her the night before, without embarrassment.

When they were about ready to leave she handed him her brush and asked, "Would you please see what you can do with my hair?"

The nurse had washed it at the hospital, so it was clean and seemed to come alive as it crackled under Matt's vigorous brushing. He smoothed it down with his hand and said, "You have beautiful hair, but that's not surprising, after all the money I've paid to Mr. David's Salon for your beauty treatments."

She was beginning to understand why Matt was so disgusted with Angela's extravagance. Anne had never had any kind of beauty treatment in her life.

They had breakfast and headed southwest out of Sterling toward Denver. The closer they got to Matt's home the more nervous Anne became. She had no idea what his parents were like, but Angela would have known them well even though she'd never met them. Apparently they had kept in fairly close touch by letter and telephone, and they and Matt had been paying all Rory and Angela's bills plus giving them a living allowance. If they had abused that generosity, as Matt seemed to feel they had, then Anne was the one who would get the scolding.

From a few things Angela had said during their brief time together, she suspected that Matt and his parents weren't happy about Rory's marriage to Angela. If that was true, how did they feel about Angela now? Matt had seemed tender and concerned at first, but as Anne grew stronger his resentment began to surface. Now, as they neared the end of their journey, he was silent and withdrawn.

Anne was too nervous to sit quietly and began to ask questions that were bothering her. "Matt, do you think your parents will like me?"

He glanced at her but didn't smile. "Of course they'll like you. You're Rory's wife."

That was no answer and she knew it. Did he mean they would love her because Rory did, or that they had to take her in whether they liked her or not because she was their youngest son's widow?

She tried again. "How did your mother and father take the news of Rory's death?"

"How do you think they took it?" His hands tightened around the leather-covered steering wheel and the twitch at the corner of his mouth reminded her once more of how painful the subject was to him. "They were shattered. We worried most about Dad with his medical history, but he's holding up pretty well."

Anne wanted to scream, *"What medical history?"*, but she didn't dare. Angela would already know what his problem was. It occurred to her that she didn't even know how old Mr. and Mrs. Hawthorne were. Were they elderly or just middle-aged? If Matt was thirty, they must be in their fifties at least. When Rory said his father owned uranium mines, she'd assumed he was still active in the business. Now Matt casually mentioned he had a "medical history." Her stomach tied itself in knots and she almost hoped they'd never arrive.

At Ft. Morgan they stopped for gas, and Anne went into the restroom to freshen up. It would be their last stop before Denver, and she delved into Angela's makeup kit. She looked in the mirror and acknowledged that there wasn't much she could do to make her face look better. The black circles around her eyes had turned a faded blueish purple and so had the bruise on her forehead.

She lined up Angela's small jars and pots and boxes of cosmetics on the sink. Angela's skin tone had been darker than Anne's. The natural color of Angela's hair had probably been brown, and her complexion had been that of a woman with dark

41

hair. Anne smoothed the foundation onto her face with her left hand, and the darker tone helped to cover the bruises. She added cheek blusher and eyebrow pencil. No need for any other eye makeup; the idea was to tone her eyes down, not highlight them. She found a shade of lipstick that complemented the emerald green pantsuit she was wearing and ran the brush through her blonde hair.

Her hands were trembling as she scooped the makeup back into Angela's purse and joined Matt back in the car. He looked at her but said nothing as she got in and closed the door.

A sign by the road said *DENVER—75 MILES*. In less than two hours they would arrive at Matthew's home. Anne's stomach knotted with apprehension. What kind of reception would she get? If Matt's mood was any indication, she wouldn't be welcomed with great joy. But that was a forgone conclusion; the family was in mourning for their youngest son. Matt had said his parents were shattered, and she could see for herself the anguish Rory's death had caused him. Anne felt cruel for taking advantage of their grief to pass herself off as their daughter-in-law. Why hadn't she given a lot more thought to this deception before she'd burned her bridges behind her? Why couldn't she bring herself to tell Matt the truth now and throw herself on his mercy? But Matt would have no mercy for a battered stranger who had deceived him as blatantly as she had. She'd be lucky if he didn't turn her over to the police right then and there.

She sighed and shifted nervously. Matt glanced at

her and said, "What's the matter with you? Why are you so nervous?"

"N—nervous?" she questioned.

"You've been twisting your fingers together and wiggling ever since we left Ft. Morgan. Relax, for Pete's sake. You're making me jumpy too."

"I'm sorry," she apologized. "It's just that I—I'm afraid to meet your parents."

Matt grunted. "They don't eat little girls for breakfast, you know."

Oh, don't they just! she thought. *If they haven't before, they will as soon as they discover I'm Anne and not Angela.*

As the miles ticked away she leaned back and tried to relax, but she was growing more and more apprehensive the closer they came to Denver. When the roadside sign said *DENVER—35 MILES,* she rummaged through Angela's purse until she found a compact and added another layer of powder to her face and touched up her lipstick.

Matt looked at her and grumbled. "You don't need to hide."

Anne was puzzled. "Hide?"

"All that makeup, it's a mask. What are you afraid of?"

Anne's good hand tightened into a fist, but she didn't answer as she turned her head and looked out at the rapidly moving snow-covered landscape. If she could only tell him what she was afraid of and know he'd understand and forgive. If only there were someone in this whole wide world in whom she could confide, but there wasn't. No family, no friends, no lovers. She was totally alone, with no one to care what happened to her. She had no one to depend on but herself, and now that she had started this charade she had to continue to act it out. After all, it wouldn't be forever. As soon as her bruises had faded so that she looked human again, she'd find a job. She wouldn't let them support her for very long.

A hand touched hers and she jumped as Matt's big hand closed over the fist in her lap. He looked at her with amazement and said, "Honestly, Anne, you're trembling!"

A tremor ran through her and Matt pulled off the highway and stopped. With an angry sigh, he reached for her and took her in his arms. She went willingly, gladly, as the nervous shivering shook her whole body. He held her close as he murmured into her hair, "Don't, Anne. What kind of monsters do you think my parents are? I'll admit none of us were very gracious when you and Rory eloped, but we've accepted you as a member of the family ever since. Why are you so frightened?"

She pressed closer against him, desperately needing the security and warmth he was so reluctantly offering. He swore softly and cradled her to him as he stroked her hair and caressed her neck and shoulders. Gradually she calmed down and her trembling subsided to an occasional tremor.

Matt kissed her temple and whispered, "You're like a terrified little girl. How old are you?"

She answered without thinking. "Twenty."

"Twenty!' He gasped as his hands stopped their

stroking. "I thought you were twenty-three last year when you were married."

Anne jerked away from him, shocked. Would she never learn to keep her guard up at all times? Now she'd really blown it. She covered her eyes with her hand and leaned forward.

"Please," she pleaded, "don't ask me questions! You know I'm twenty-four, so why ask? Are you *trying* to confuse me?"

He took her in his arms again and held her as he said, "Of course I'm not trying to confuse you. It's just that you seem so young. If I didn't know better I'd believe you are only twenty."

Once again his softly stroking hands calmed her. She could feel his heart beating in time with her own, but when his arms tightened and his breathing became jerky he pushed her away. "Much as I'm enjoying this I'm afraid we're going to have to drive on. For one thing, the highway patrol will find us soon and want to know what the trouble is, and for another . . ." His voice trailed into silence.

Matt started the car again, and by the time the Denver skyline appeared in the distance, she was feeling drowsy and relaxed.

Anne had never been in Denver before. She and Matt had been traveling across a flat prairie that gradually but steadily climbed, and now they were a mile above sea level. Even so, the skyscrapers that towered above the city were dwarfed by the Rocky Mountains rising directly behind them. Matt pointed out the gold-domed state capitol building and explained that the gold on the dome wasn't just gilt but solid twenty-eight-carat gold leaf from the mines in the Rockies.

They drove through the traffic-laden city streets until they reached an area of beautiful large homes on equally large lots. The circular driveway they finally turned into was in front of a huge, brick, two-story mansion set well back on at least two acres of snow-covered land amid ancient, gnarled trees that stood naked, with nests of frozen snow in their branches.

Matt stopped the car, and almost immediately the massive hand-carved oak doors opened and a burly man, built like a boxer, came hurrying down the steps that were flanked on either side by terraced gardens, empty now and covered with snow. He grinned as he opened the car door on Anne's side but greeted Matt.

"We've been watching for you, Mr. Matt, and I don't mind telling you I'm glad you're here. Handling the calls and visitors and cards is getting to be too much for your dad. He insists he's all right, but his blood pressure's up again."

Matt frowned as he got out of the car. "Why isn't Lester taking care of that stuff? That's what he was hired for."

The other man shrugged. "Mr. James won't let him, says it's not right to let a secretary handle such personal matters."

Matt got out of the car and walked around to help Anne. She took his hand and climbed awkwardly out of the car, still clumsy, with her right hand useless in a cast and sling. Matt made the introductions.

"Anne, this is Wolfgang Gabbert, Dad's attendant. Wolf, I'd like you to meet Angela, Rory's . . . widow."

The man took her free hand in his and said, "I'm pleased to meet you, Mrs. Rory, but sorry it has to be under these circumstances. And call me Wolf, everyone does."

Anne watched Wolf as he pulled the suitcases from the trunk and led the way up the stairs to the house. He was one of those men who looked ageless. He could be thirty or fifty or anywhere in between. He wasn't tall, but he had a powerful build. His broad shoulders and chest had muscles that rippled even through the wool plaid shirt he was wearing. His light brown hair was close cropped in an old army style cut, and his gray eyes were respectful but hinted that he expected respect in return. Anne was sure she was going to like him, but what kind of attendant was he and why did Mr. Hawthorne need him?

Wolf held the door open while Matt's hand on the elbow of Anne's broken arm gently guided her into the house. She gazed in awe at the luxurious entryway. It was twice the size of Aunt Martha's small living room, with tile in subdued shades of rust and brown on the floor and a thickly carpeted stairway along the right wall leading upward to easily imagined opulence. Portraits of distinguished-looking men and women marched up the wall beside the stairs.

There was a massive Victorian style sofa along the left wall and above it an oil painting of the Rocky Mountain landscape. Directly ahead of them, in an alcove between two hallways that apparently led to the back of the house, a larger-than-life-sized marble bust stood beside an antique chest that had a heavy gold-framed mirror hanging above it. Anne knew nothing about antiques and art, but she recognized these as authentic. There would be no copies in this house.

The most startling feature of the room, however, was the magnificent crystal chandelier that hung from the high ceiling. The light from the candle-shaped bulbs was reflected by the dangling crystal teardrops and sparkled brilliantly on the walls.

Anne stared in speechless wonder until Matt's sharp, cold voice broke the silence. "Impressive, isn't it?"

She looked up, startled, as he continued. "My mother seems intent on turning this place into a museum. You and she should get along fine. You both spend money like it was going out of style."

Before she could react to the bitterness of his words, he'd turned to Wolf and asked, "Where's my father?"

Wolf answered, "I think I hear him coming now."

There was a soft whirring sound and a large, white-haired man in a wheelchair appeared in the doorway to the right of the alcove. He was wearing a navy blue wool sport shirt, open at the neck, and his left arm was held close to his side, the hand limp in his lap. There was a blanket over his legs and he wore leather slippers on his feet. His eyes, as he regarded Anne, were dark pools of bleakness and despair, and his face was white and lined with sadness.

Matt spoke first. "Anne, I'd like you to meet my father, James Hawthorne. Dad, this is Angela."

Anne was trying to deal with the shock of finding Matt's father in a wheelchair. What was wrong with him? Angela would have known, but how could Anne possibly talk to him without saying the wrong thing, giving herself away?

Would this nightmare never end?

Chapter Three

James Hawthorne held out his right hand to Anne, and she took it in her good left hand as he said, "Welcome, Angela. You look like you shouldn't be out of the hospital yet. Would you like to go right to your room? We can talk later."

The smile that had been hovering around Anne's mouth disappeared. *So much for my makeup repair job,* she thought. *I must still look dreadful.* But did she really look so ill or was this just Mr. Hawthorne's way of getting rid of her so he could talk to Matt, find out what kind of little baggage she was and how long they were apt to be stuck with her? She felt the coldness of rejection as she slipped her hand from his and said, "Thank you, Mr. Hawthorne, I think I will go upstairs now."

Matt frowned as he studied her closely and said, "I'll show you to your room."

He took Anne's arm as James Hawthorne protested. "No need for that, Matt. I'll have Bess take her up. I've arranged for Bess to be Angela's personal maid, at least until she's out of that cast."

Matt's hand tightened on Anne's arm. "Fine. Anne needs a maid, but I'll show her to her room. Send Bess up in about ten minutes. I'll meet you in the den then." He started to lead Anne toward the stairway, then stopped. "By the way, where's Mother?"

James shrugged. "She has another of her headaches and is spending the day in bed. She'll send for Angela when she feels up to talking to her."

Matt swore softly and led Anne up the staircase.

At the top of the stairs was a landing the size of a room, with more oil paintings and smaller statues on marble columns. A rose window on the outside wall overlooked the front lawn and must have been imported from one of the cathedrals of Europe. Anne felt ridiculously out of place, like a street urchin in a palace. A hall ran to the right and left, the full width of the house, and Matt turned to the left and led her down the corridor. At the last door they stopped.

It was a southwest corner room with windows on both the front of the house and the west side. The furnishings here were antique as well, but delicate and feminine. A four-poster canopied bed, writing desk and chair, tall, slender lingerie chest with a myriad of small drawers, a larger chest and a dressing table with a framed mirror took up only part of the area in the spacious room.

Two modern upholstered lounge chairs and a round table, draped with floor-length pink-flowered chintz, were grouped in the corner between the two windows. A smaller round table stood beside the bed, and both held lamps that were old and probably priceless. The pink-flowered chintz was repeated in the bedspread, canopy cover and curtains, and the floor was covered with shag carpeting in a warm beige. It was breathtakingly beautiful, but again Anne felt uneasy and out of place. She had the feeling that if she broke or scratched anything, it would be a hanging offense.

Matt led her into the room and turned her toward him as he said, "I'm sorry you didn't get a warmer welcome, Anne, but losing Rory was a terrible blow for Dad and Mother. Please, try to understand and give them a little time."

He really seemed concerned about her feelings, and she nodded and answered, "Of course, I understand. I'll try to stay out of their way."

"That's not what I meant," he rasped, as he unbuttoned her fake fur cape and removed it. He opened the louvered doors of the closet, and Anne saw that it was filled with clothes. Matt didn't seem surprised as he hung up her coat and said, "I see your things arrived."

She stared in amazement. "My things?"

He looked at her. "Yes. Didn't I tell you I'd made arrangements to have all the personal things in your apartment in Cambridge shipped here? Fortunately, you were renting it furnished, so we didn't have the bother of moving furniture, too. I hope you don't mind, but I took the liberty of asking the lawyer to sell your Trans-Am. It wouldn't have been practical to transport it back here. As soon as you can drive again, you can buy a new one."

Anne hadn't the vaguest idea what he was talking about. Had all those clothes belonged to Angela? How could she possibly have worn them all? And a sports car? Oh, no, why did everything have to be so complicated? She couldn't wear Angela's clothes, or buy a new car with the money from Angela's old one. She didn't have the right.

As if from a distance, she heard Matt talking. "Anne, what's the matter? You look like you've never seen those clothes before. They *are* yours, aren't they? The neighbor who packed them didn't make a mistake, did she?"

Anne came out of her daze and tried to sound intelligent. "No. Yes. I mean yes, of course they're my clothes. I was just surprised to see them. I—I—thank you."

Matt looked at her closely. "Are you all right? You do look worn out. Bess will be here in a minute. You'd better let her undress you and put you to bed." He grinned rakishly. "Or would you rather let me do that?"

She grinned back. "I told you last night I'd rather have you."

The grin was gone and his eyes held her motionless as his long fingers began to unfasten the first button on her blouse. A rap on the door and a soft female voice broke the spell.

"It's me; Bess. May I come in?"

Matt opened the door and admitted the woman standing there, then left without a word and shut the door behind him.

Bess was plump, cheerful and about forty. She was dressed in dark slacks and a blue print smock that Anne was to learn was the standard uniform of the household help. She surveyed the situation and within minutes had run steamy water into the claw-footed bathtub in Anne's private pink bathroom and washed her like a baby, careful not to get the cast on her arm wet. She brought one of Angela's sexy nighties and helped an embarrassed Anne into it, then tucked her into bed with orders to sleep. Anne didn't need to have the order repeated.

It was dark when she woke to a knock on the door and a voice calling, "Mrs. Rory, it's Bess. Are you awake?"

For a moment Anne lay there waiting for someone to answer. When the knock and question were repeated she realized Bess was calling her. She remembered Wolf calling her Mrs. Rory earlier and knew she'd better get used to answering to it. That was apparently the name by which all the household staff would refer to her.

She called, "Come in." The door opened and the room was flooded with light from the overhead chandelier, smaller than the one in the entryway but delicate, old and obviously valuable.

Bess wheeled in a tea cart containing a large bed tray with a coffee server and several covered dishes on it. She greeted Anne and helped her to sit up as she arranged the tray across her legs and said, "Mrs.

54

Hawthorne thought you might want your dinner in bed tonight. She's having hers in her room, too, and she asked me to tell you she's sorry she hasn't felt up to seeing you today but she hopes to be feeling better by tomorrow."

Anne thanked her and removed the cover from a bowl of fragrant vegetable soup. It was possible that Mrs. Hawthorne really was too ill to see her, but Anne was sure that Angela's mother-in-law didn't want to meet the unsuitable girl her son had married against his family's wishes. So far Anne had managed to convince Matt that she was his sister-in-law and Rory's father hadn't shown any interest in her at all, but would she be able to fool another woman? Especially Rory's adoring mother? She shivered and tried to distract her thoughts by talking to Bess, who was unpacking the elegant powder blue suitcase Matt had bought her in Nebraska.

"Bess, did Mr. Hawthorne and Matt have their dinner in the dining room?"

"Yes, they're eating now. They went out this afternoon and just got home about half an hour ago."

Anne was surprised. "Went out? But Mr. Hawthorne . . . does he leave the house?"

"Oh, yes." Bess was putting a stack of lacy panties in one of the drawers of the lingerie chest. "It's been six months since he had his stroke. He still gets tired easy, but the doctors tell him to get out and around, see people and live as normally as possible. It's difficult for him, though, without the use of his left arm and leg."

So that was Matt's father's problem, a stroke. A fairly recent one, too. It would have happened since Rory and Angela were married. Anne felt sympathy welling up for the white-haired man in the wheelchair whom she had spoken to so briefly. "Will he always be paralyzed?"

Bess snapped the empty suitcase shut and put it in the closet. "The doctor says he would be able to use his arm and leg if he would do the exercises Wolf teaches him, but he hardly ever does. Says they're just a waste of time and he'll always be useless. Now, since Mr. Rory—" her voice broke and she didn't finish the sentence. "Well, he just sits in his den alone. Gets real mad if anyone comes in and sees him." She turned to leave, wishing Anne a good night as she went.

She didn't wake until ten o'clock the next morning, and then it was to Bess's cheerful knock. The older woman entered the room carrying a tray bearing a carafe of orange juice and a pot of coffee.

"Good morning, Mrs. Rory. Mrs. Hawthorne sent up a light breakfast. We'll be serving lunch at twelve-thirty."

Anne thanked her and asked her to set the tray on the table while she went to the bathroom to wash and brush her teeth. As she bathed her face with warm, clear water, she studied it in the mirror. The bruises were fading quite rapidly and she looked much more rested. She felt better, too. The bruises on her body were still big and ugly, but they could be covered, and her ribs hardly hurt at all anymore. Her arm no longer throbbed with pain either, but the heavy cast was an encumbrance she found frustrating and the sling rubbed the back of her neck.

Bess was gone when Anne returned to the bedroom, but she had made the bed and laid out the peignoir that matched the nightgown Anne was wearing. Anne slipped it on and swirled in front of the full-length mirror. It was the most beautiful outfit she had ever worn. The buttercup yellow brought out amber flecks in her brown eyes, and in spite of the bruises she looked dainty and feminine.

She made a face as she sat down at the table and poured the ice-cold orange juice. She would have liked to have gone downstairs for breakfast. She was getting tired of being cooped up in her room, but Mrs. Hawthorne seemed determined to keep her there. Was Angela being punished for daring to marry Rory?

She was letting her imagination run away with her, she told herself. It was only natural that Mrs. Hawthorne would be concerned about her and want her to rest as much as possible. After all, she'd just gotten out of the hospital and then taken the long trip to Denver. Mrs. Hawthorne was grieving for her son and she had every reason to believe that Anne was grieving also. Anyway, she'd be going downstairs for lunch.

Anne finished her juice and coffee and decided to explore the closet and determine the extent of her new wardrobe. She gasped as she pushed aside the louvered doors. The huge closet was filled with clothes. There were racks of dresses, both long and short, all in soft and expensive materials; dozens of skirts and jeans, and tops in every color imaginable.

There were shoes of every description, from slippers to boots, and jackets, chunky cardigan sweaters and a blonde camel-hair wraparound coat, not to mention the mink and leather coats Matt had mentioned. Anne, who had never before had more than two pair of jeans and one good dress at a time, was stunned. How could anyone need so many clothes?

She closed the doors and rummaged through the dresser drawers till she found a large assortment of makeup. It was like the cosmetic counter in a department store. She selected shades that would suit her and applied them sparingly, using just enough to lighten the bruises and add a little color to her lips. She was getting better at brushing her hair with her left hand and was fluffing up the ends when Bess came with another tray of food and an apologetic look. "Mrs. Hawthorne asked me to bring your lunch up here."

Anne had an urge to throw the brush she was holding. Not again! Was she never going to get out of this room and be a part of the family? After all, they thought she was their daughter-in-law. She might just as well be locked in a tower. She was a stranger in a strange place and didn't feel free to roam around the house until she was invited to do so. Did Mrs. Hawthorne think she could avoid meeting her son's widow forever?

She muttered angrily under her breath and directed Bess to set the tray on the table. Bess looked up from arranging the table setting and a smile lit up her face as she said, "You look nice, Mrs. Rory. Those bruises are fading—"

She was cut off in midsentence when the door banged open and Matt, his eyes blazing, came storming in shouting, "Anne, I've had enough of your nonsense! You've been sulking in your room long enough. Now cut out this act you're putting on and get downstairs!"

She was standing behind him and he swung around looking for her. When he saw her he stood with his mouth open, but no words came. He finally shut it and looked her over carefully, from the top of her shining blonde hair down the sunny yellow peignoir to the matching slippers and back up again. The look in his eyes turned to admiration as he whistled and said, "Well, our little waif is a full-grown beauty! No wonder you could wrap Rory around those tiny fingers of yours."

She forgot his angry words of a minute ago and smiled. "Do you really like the way I look?"

His eyes once more took inventory and lingered teasingly on the rise of her breasts beneath the gauze-like material. His voice was lazily sensuous as he answered, "I'd have to be a robot not to. I have all the same urges my brother had, you know."

He tore his eyes away from her and now his voice was hard again. "I'm not Rory, though, so don't waste your time trying to seduce me."

She shrank back as though he had hit her as he continued, "We've put up with your little tantrum long enough. I'll admit Dad and Mother didn't put themselves out to greet you when you arrived, but they had a good excuse. They don't deserve either your sulky silence or your insistence on being waited on. Who do you think you are, anyway? I can understand your being too tired to have dinner with us last night, but breakfast and lunch in bed is going too far." He looked at his gold wristwatch. "Lunch is being served in the dining room in fifteen minutes. Be there!"

He turned and stalked out, leaving Anne staring after him, stunned and bewildered.

Bess was as shocked as Anne, but once the door slammed behind Matt she recovered quickly. There was fire in her eyes as she said, "The man must be out of his mind! Mrs. Hawthorne told me herself to bring your meals up here!" She started to move toward the door. "I'll catch him and explain."

Anne moved quickly to stop her. "No, Bess, don't bother. Matt doesn't like me. I don't know why, but he's determined to think the worst of me. Let it go. Everyone is upset enough right now."

Bess started to protest, but Anne cut her off as panic rose to the surface. "Oh, Bess, what should I wear when I go down? How do they dress for lunch around here?"

Bess soothed her and picked out a pumpkin-toned dress with wide dolman sleeves that fit over her cast. A matching belt cinched in her tiny waist, and they found high-heeled pumps of the same color. Apparently all of Angela's dresses had shoes dyed to match. Anne breathed a sigh of relief as she slipped her foot in the pump and found it was a perfect fit.

Bess searched through one of the lingerie drawers and found a large patterned scarf in complementary colors that they used as a sling for Anne's arm. It was a definite improvement over the hospital bandage. With a quick pat to be sure her hair was smooth, she started out the door, then remembered. She hadn't any idea how to get to the dining room.

Bess laughed and escorted her down the stairs and through the door to their left into a cavernous drawing room furnished with fragile, highly polished antiques that Anne made no attempt to identify. There were pictures in ornate frames, figurines too precious to touch, and in one corner of the room an odd piano-like instrument that she later learned was a harpsicord. The walls, carpet and draperies were eggshell white and showed the lovely woods to advantage.

The three people in the room turned to look at her. Matt was standing by the marble fireplace with a glass in his hand. His father was sitting by the window in his wheelchair, and the lovely dark-haired woman sitting stiffly in the straight-backed chair had to be Matt's mother. Rory's mother.

For a moment Anne was tempted to turn and run, but then she saw the reluctant approval in Matt's eyes as he said, "Well, I'm glad to see you can follow orders and be on time."

He put down his glass and came across the room toward her. With his hand on the elbow of her broken arm he turned her to face the woman and said, "Mother, this is Angela. Angela, my mother, Constance."

The woman sitting in front of her was of medium height with dark hair brushed back into a French twist. The severe style accentuated the almost

61

perfect features of her oval face, touched only faintly with grief. She was immaculately dressed in dark gray relieved only by a string of creamy pearls at her throat. In one graceful movement she stood up, making no attempt to disguise the distaste in her eyes as she said, "How nice you feel up to joining us, Angela. I hope your room is comfortable and you have everything you need."

Everything but a warm welcome, thought Anne. Mrs. Hawthorne had received her as she would receive any unwelcome guest. No apology for not having greeted her sooner, not a word to indicate they were happy to have their daughter-in-law with them, only the barest formal politeness. The nagging little voice that was Anne's conscience told her it was still more than she deserved, but she shut it out, telling herself that as Angela she had a right to be considered a member of the family. She owed it to Angela's memory not to let Rory's family treat her this way. She smiled slightly and said, "Thank you, Mrs. Hawthorne, for insisting I have my meals in my room, but I would have been happy to join you at any time. I was only waiting for an invitation."

She felt Matt stiffen beside her, but his mother merely eyed her coldly and said, "This is your home now. I shouldn't think you'd need an invitation to join the family."

Anne bit her lip. She should have known she was no match for this self-possessed older woman who was used to getting her own way.

She slumped and turned away when she noticed Mr. Hawthorne still sitting by the window. He hadn't spoken and seemed lost in a world of his own. For a minute she was tempted to ignore him as he seemed to be ignoring her, but then she decided that just because the Hawthornes were boorish and bad-mannered, there was no reason for her to be so as well. She walked over to the man sitting in the wheelchair and said, "Good afternoon, Mr. Hawthorne. Do you remember me? We met briefly the other day."

He looked up at her, surprised, then smiled slightly and answered. "Of course we did, and I've been looking forward to seeing you again. I hope you're feeling better now."

Anne breathed a little sigh of relief. He was actually being nice to her! She smiled back. "I'm fine, thank you, although my arm still hurts a bit."

Just then a bell tinkled from somewhere in the house and Matt, sounding somewhat irritated, said, "Lunch is served. Shall we go to the dining room?"

Lunch consisted of grilled pork chops, rice pilaf and a molded salad, with cranberry ice for dessert. It was delicious, but Anne was too intimidated to enjoy it. The dining room was directly across the entryway from the living room and almost as large. It too looked out on the front lawn, across that vast expanse of snow-covered grounds and trees. The furniture, here as in the other rooms, was highly polished antiques. Anne thought this room might be done in a French period but couldn't be sure. What little she knew about antiques she had learned in a course on interior decorating she had taken in high school. Their places were set with sterling silver and china, and a glass-fronted china cabinet was filled with crystal, china and fragile Dresden figurines. An ornate sterling-silver coffee and tea service on a huge silver tray sat on the massive sideboard, flanked on either side by tall vases of red roses and holly leaves, and the centerpiece on the table was an arrangement of red and white roses.

Anne wondered if she'd ever get used to living in such sumptuous surroundings. She doubted it. For one thing, she was afraid to touch anything. She hesitated to drink her coffee for fear of breaking the cup. That one little cup probably cost more than the whole set of crockery her great aunt treasured as her "good dishes."

For another thing, everyone was so stiff and formal. There was nothing to suggest intimacy. The table was huge, and with only four of them around it they couldn't possibly touch each other even if they'd wanted to. There was even a maid to cut up the meat for Mr. Hawthorne and Anne and to pass dishes around. It would be a grand place to entertain a lot of dinner guests, but she couldn't imagine eating all her meals there.

Anne became aware of Matt's eyes on her from across the table and looked up. He was frowning. "You're not eating much. Don't you like the food?"

She put down the spoon she'd been using to push her cranberry ice around in the crystal stemware. "Oh, yes, the food's delicious. I—I'm just not very hungry."

Constance Hawthorne glanced at her haughtily. "I

think it would have been best if you'd spent another day or so in bed. Possibly the excitement of being up and around is too much."

An angry sputter came from the other end of the table and they all looked toward Mr. Hawthorne, who threw his napkin down and roared, "For heaven's sake, leave the poor child alone! She doesn't have to eat if she doesn't want to. I can't say that I blame her. Eating here is like dining out in a morgue!"

Constance gasped, but he paid no attention as he pushed the button on the arm of this electric wheelchair and backed away from the table. He turned once more to Anne.

"If you've finished, Angela, come with me; I want to talk to you. Matt will join us in the den later, when he's finished his lunch."

He looked from Matt to his wife. "I'm sure you'll excuse us."

Anne jumped up from the table, bewildered, and ran after him as his wheelchair rolled out of the room.

They went diagonally across the entryway and down the hall on the right. Anne glimpsed a bathroom in shades of green, and about halfway down the hall they turned right down a connecting hall. On one side was a wide arch that led into the drawing room, and on the other side were two rooms. The first was lined with book shelves, but it was into the second that Mr. Hawthorne led her. It was a large room by most standards, but much smaller than the others she had been in. There was a feeling of intimacy about it, with its dark paneling and the cheery fire in the brick fireplace. There were no antiques here, just well-built, comfortable furniture. One whole wall was glass, with sliding doors that led onto a covered patio. It was covered with sheer floor-to-ceiling curtains, and heavy burgundy drapes could be pulled to cover the entire area.

James Hawthorne pulled a cord on the wall and almost immediately Wolf appeared to help him from his wheelchair onto the creamy velour couch in front of the fire. James was a big man, at least as tall as Matt, and by using his good arm and leg he managed the transfer with surprising grace.

He patted the seat beside him and said, "Sit down, Angela, and relax. We won't be disturbed here. No one's allowed in my den without an invitation."

Anne sat beside him and smiled. "Please, Mr. Hawthorne, call me Anne. It's the name I've always gone by."

He grinned. "All right, Anne, if you'll quit calling me 'Mr. Hawthorne.' You can call me Dad if you like, but if you're uncomfortable with that, why don't you call me Jim? I like it better than James, although I do use that for business purposes."

"Are—are you sure?" said Anne uncertainly.

He patted her hand. "Very sure. How can we be close friends if you call me 'Mr. Hawthorne'?"

Anne laughed, delighted by his casual banter. "I guess we can't, can we—Jim?"

The loneliness that looked out of his dark eyes, so

like Matt's, lightened a little as he said, "Tell me about yourself, Anne. I know you were working as a waitress when you married Rory and that you have no family, but I want to know about the years when you were growing up."

Anne hesitated. If he knew nothing about Angela's background, then she wouldn't have to make one up. She could tell him the truth about herself, Anne Greenfield, and not have to lie.

"My parents were killed when I was four years old," she began, "and I was raised by a great aunt who disliked children but had a strong sense of duty. She never let me forget the sacrifices she made or the money she spent on me during the years I was growing up."

Anne shivered at the memory. "I suppose she meant well, but she instilled in me a deep sense of guilt for disrupting her life and then used it like a club to make me do her bidding. I was her unpaid servant until—" Now she'd have to remember Angela's past and invent a story to match it. She'd try to keep it brief. "Until I was old enough to be on my own. Then I got a job as a waitress and worked until I met Rory."

She prayed he wouldn't question her about her life with Rory. He didn't get the chance. A caustic voice from behind them interrupted. "That's a sad story but not unusual. A lot of people have unhappy childhoods."

She turned around to see Matt standing behind the couch holding a tray with yet another coffee server and three cups. He obviously wasn't prepared

67

to offer her sympathy. Well, that was fine, she didn't want it.

She lifted her chin as he came around and put the tray down on the low coffee table. "Of course they do, and they manage to survive just as I did, without rich parents and palatial homes."

Matt grimaced good naturedly. "Ouch! I gather that barb was aimed at me?"

Jim frowned. "If it wasn't, it should have been; you deserved it! Now keep a civil tongue in your head and sit down so we can discuss the funeral arrangements with Anne."

"Funeral!" The word was out before she could call it back, but Jim didn't seem to notice her shock.

"Yes, of course, my dear. We've been waiting until you were well enough, but we can't put if off any longer. We've scheduled Rory's funeral for the day after tomorrow at eleven o'clock."

Oh, no! She hadn't even thought of a funeral! If it had entered her mind at all she had assumed it had been held while she was still in the hospital. But of course they wouldn't lay Rory to rest without his widow and his brother present. How could she have been so stupid?

What was she going to do now? She would have to play the part of Rory's grieving widow at a gathering of all his friends and relatives. How did widows act at funerals? Did they bear up bravely, or break down and have hysterics? She couldn't possibly fake a scene like that.

For the hundredth time she wondered why she'd ever gotten herself into this. It had seemed so simple in the beginning, just go along with Matt's assumption that she was Rory's wife, Angela, until she was better and could take care of herself. But now the lies and deceptions were piling up, building a wall that one day soon—too soon—might fall and crush her!

Chapter Four

Anne had never seen so many well-dressed, affluent people gathered in one place before. The funeral parlor was large but the crowd was larger, and it spilled over into an adjoining room where a public-address system had been set up. Someone said the governor and his family were there, and for the first time Anne realized just how rich and powerful the Hawthorne family must be. Had all these people actually known Rory or were they here to pay their respects to James Hawthorne?

Matt led his mother into the family seating area, and Anne and Wolf walked on either side of Jim in his wheelchair. The small room was filled with brothers and sisters of the senior Hawthornes, nieces and nephews, cousins and even an elderly aunt. Some of them had arrived the day before and had stayed at the house. Anne had taken refuge in her room, this time voluntarily, after being introduced.

No one seemed to mind. She had seen Jim and Matt only fleetingly since they had explained the funeral arrangements to her in the den.

Matt took his mother's sable coat and handed it to an attendant. Wolf was helping Jim out of his overcoat, and Anne was left to struggle with the buttons on Angela's stunning mink with her left hand. It was the first time she'd worn either of Angela's fur coats. She hadn't intended to wear them at all, but when she had come downstairs that morning in the fake fur cape Matt had bought her, Mrs. Hawthorne had looked at her with blue eyes as icy as her voice and said, "Surely you don't intend to wear that cheap imitation to your husband's funeral?"

Anne had been suffering from attacks of nerves over how she should act at the funeral but not over what she should wear. One of the few dresses in Angela's wardrobe that had sleeves wide enough to fit over Anne's cast was a Kelly-green wool with a high neckline and a slim skirt. Bess had found her a green, brown and yellow print scarf to wear as a sling, and with the matching shoes and the fake fur cape, she'd thought she looked presentable. Now, with one sentence, Mrs. Hawthorne had destroyed that illusion completely.

"I—I—what's the matter with it?" Anne stammered as Matt detached himself from the two men he was talking to a few feet away and joined Anne and his mother.

He looked from one to the other and said, "What's wrong?"

Mrs. Hawthorne told him. "I won't have Angela

71

wearing that cheap coat to the funeral." Her gaze dropped to the skirt of the dress that showed below the hip-length cape. "And that dress is all wrong, too. It's too bright. Why aren't you wearing black?" she demanded.

Anne shrank back and her voice shook as she said, "But I don't have a black dress." She looked at Matt. "This is the most suitable outfit I have that will fit over my cast."

Matt removed the coat from her shoulders and looked at her for a minute, then turned to his mother. "There's nothing wrong with Anne's dress. It looks very nice on her, and you know perfectly well that few people wear black to funerals anymore."

Mrs. Hawthorne, who was dressed all in black, gave her son a withering glance. "I suppose if she hasn't anything suitable, that will have to do, but I know she has other coats and I insist she change."

She walked swiftly away and managed a sad smile for the man and woman who called out to her.

Near tears from humiliation, Anne turned to go to her room for another coat and bumped into Matt. His arm circled her slender waist and he drew her against him, saying, "Stay right here. I'll send someone for another wrap."

He signaled Bess, who had just come into the room, and told her what he wanted.

Anne snuggled into the protection of his strong arm around her and whispered brokenly, "I'm sorry. I didn't mean to embarrass your mother. I thought I looked all right." She swallowed a sob. "I love that cape and it fits so well."

His arm tightened and he murmured into her hair, "You look lovely. Rory would have been proud of you, but let's humor Mother about the coat. She's a little unstrung, you know."

So the day had started out badly, and she was sure it would get worse instead of better. The cast wouldn't fit into the arm of the mink coat, so she had worn it over her shoulders, buttoned cape style, although it was awkward. She gave up trying to unbutton the buttons and decided to leave the coat on. It was warm in the room, but since Mrs. Hawthorne objected to her dress, it was best to keep it covered.

There was a constant murmur of voices as relatives greeted each other and found seats. Anne was standing watching Wolf help Jim from the wheelchair to the settee when Matt's voice sounded behind her.

"Turn around and I'll unbutton your coat."

She turned and looked at him but shook her head. "I'd better leave it on."

He muttered impatiently and started to undo the buttons. "Don't be silly; it's much too warm to wear that heavy thing in here."

She clutched at it as he tried to remove it from her shoulders, and he said, "You don't need to hide, Anne. You're the most beautiful woman here. Ask any of the men if you don't believe me."

He walked off with the coat, leaving her alone again.

She had thought Mr. and Mrs. Hawthorne would sit together, but when she glanced around she saw Mrs. Hawthorne sitting on a sofa a few feet away. As she watched, Matt seated himself beside his mother, so Anne sank down on the seat beside Jim. He turned to look at her and her heart melted at the sight of his white, drawn, grief-stricken face. She hoped he wouldn't notice the absence of a corresponding grief in her own features.

She touched his arm and said, "Jim, are you going to be all right?"

He nodded. "I'm not sick or anything like that, Anne, but you might prefer to sit somewhere else. I haven't had much control over my emotions since the stroke and I may break down and embarrass you."

She hugged his arm and said, "If I don't embarrass you, you sure won't embarrass me."

He reached up with his good hand and patted her cheek.

The service seemed interminable. The organ music was soothing and peaceful and Anne leaned back in the comfortable seat and drifted along with the melody. Then came the obituary, and the tears Jim had been fighting to hold back rolled down his ashen cheeks. Anne put her hand in his and he gripped it and bit his lip. She glanced back at Matt and saw that a beautiful, dark-haired young woman had joined him and his mother on the couch. The woman and Matt were holding hands, but he was looking at his mother, sitting straight and silent on the other side of him. Anne wondered who the woman was and her stomach muscles knotted into an unfamiliar tightness. She could be a relative, but somehow Anne didn't think so.

At last the service was over and the mourners

were filing past the closed casket. The family formed a line in front of Jim and Anne and accepted condolences. Wolf made use of the distraction to help Jim into his overcoat and back into the wheel chair. Anne asked the attendant to bring her coat, and the three of them started toward the back exit from the room.

It was then that Matt broke from the line and hurried toward them. "Where are you going? It will be a while yet before we can leave for the cemetery."

Anne shook her head. "We're not going to the cemetery; we're taking your father home."

Matt looked at her through pain-filled eyes. She suspected that he had lost the battle to tears, too. He said, "I agree Dad should go on home, but Anne, you're Rory's wife! Surely you want to go to the cemetery for the graveside service? Wolf will go with Dad."

Anne knew she was behaving suspiciously, but her concern for Jim overrode her caution. As she spoke, she wondered if she could make Matt understand. "Rory doesn't need me anymore, Matt, but Jim does."

Matt looked at her with narrowed eyes. "Jim? Since when have you been calling my father Jim?"

Anne ignored the question. "I'm going home with him; that is, unless your mother suddenly remembers she has a husband who needs his wife," she finished bitterly as she turned and walked away.

At home the caterers were busy setting out a buffet lunch for the dozens of friends and relatives who would be coming by after the funeral to offer

75

their condolences and visit. Jim refused to be taken upstairs in the elevator that had been installed for his convenience, and insisted instead on going to the den. He explained that he wanted to be on hand to greet their guests when they came.

Wolf helped him to lie down on the couch in front of the fire and loosened his tie before covering him with an afghan and leaving. Anne sat on a plump cushion on the floor beside the couch and took his hand in hers as she said, "Are you feeling better now?"

"How could I not feel better with a daughter like you to comfort me?" Jim brought her closer with his good arm and she put her head down on his shoulder. "I suspect that you are fast becoming indispensable to the men in this household, and that could cause a great deal of havoc."

Anne wasn't sure what he was talking about, but she knew he liked her and she relaxed at last. He'd called her his daughter. She didn't remember her own father and had never known a man's guidance and concern. Jim was kind and gentle and needed a daughter as badly as she needed a father. Surely there could be no harm in letting herself love him?

The drapes had been pulled against the gray and windy day, and the only light was the light from the blazing fire in the red brick fireplace. The fire crackled and popped with such an intimate, homey sound, and Jim's firm shoulder under her cheek, his arm holding her, filled her with such contentment that she sighed drowsily and they both slept.

She was wakened by a hand shaking her shoulder

and Matt's harsh voice. "Wake up, Anne. I'd advise you not to let my mother find you sleeping in Dad's arms like this."

She jerked upright, confused, as Jim spoke in a voice as harsh as Matt's. "Shut your mouth, Matthew, before I shut it for you! If you can't keep your jealousy under control, at least have the decency not to take it out on Anne."

"Jealousy?" Matt roared. "You and Rory may be soft in the head, but I see through her easily enough!"

By this time Anne had scrambled to her feet, confused at first but slowly realizing the implication of what the two men were shouting at each other. She felt the warm flush of outrage as Matt's accusations finally sank in. She turned to rush out of the room but bumped into Wolf, who had just come in. By the time she'd backed away from him, Matt was at her side, his hand gripping her wrist.

"Where do you think you're going?" he hissed.

She struggled to pull away. "I'm going to my room."

His fingers tightened until she gasped with pain. "Oh, no, you're not. You're going to stay down here and belatedly act like a grief-stricken widow. I'm tired of making excuses for you. If you're not in the drawing room in ten minutes I'm coming to get you." He dropped his hand and stalked out.

When she entered the drawing room exactly ten minutes later, Matt came toward her, and she knew he had been watching for her. He wasn't alone, however. The dark-haired charmer who had been with him at the funeral was hanging possessively onto his arm, and he introduced them.

"Polly, I don't believe you've met my sister-in-law, Angela. Anne, this is Polly Parker, the loveliest of our local television newscasters."

So, she was a television personality, a celebrity. Anne wasn't surprised. Polly had a professional air to her beauty. She was tall and slender and wore her royal blue dress with its blouson top and swirling skirt like a model. Her eyes matched the dress and her smooth, creamy complexion was a startling contrast to her elegantly styled black hair. She made no secret of the fact that she considered Matt her own exclusive property, and Matt didn't act as if he minded at all. Anne felt a stabbing pain somewhere in the region of her heart.

After the two women greeted each other, Matt took Anne by the arm and kept her with them as they moved from group to group so he could introduce her. Anne was aware that, at least to Polly, she was an unwelcome third, and the thought gave her a perverse pleasure.

Polly was known to everyone there, and it soon became evident that she and Matt were a twosome of long standing. When talking with other young couples in the crowd, Polly made a point of reminiscing about weekends they had spent skiing at Aspen or the vacation they had taken to Hawaii.

The thought of Matt and Polly sharing vacations was like a physical pain, and Anne was afraid she was going to be sick. She glanced around the room, noisy with the hum of voices, the clink of glasses and the laughter that erupted in spite of the solemnity of the occasion. Her vision was blocked by well-educated pillars of business and society milling around discussing finances with some, sports with others, and exchanging gossip with all. The air was thick with smoke and Anne's eyes burned as she pushed her way through the press of expensively perfumed bodies.

In the entryway she saw Constance Hawthorne walking beside Jim in his wheelchair as they circulated among the rooms, visiting with their friends. Anne relaxed a little. At last Matt's mother had remembered she had a husband and was acting like a wife.

After about half an hour the crowd congregated around the bar and the buffet table, and Anne managed to pull away from Matt and go off on her own. For a minute she was afraid he'd come after her, but Polly distracted him. A stout, middle-aged matron stopped her to ask where she could find a mirror to repair her lipstick, and by the time Anne had directed her to the powder room, Matt and Polly were out of sight.

The crowd in the drawing room had thinned out, and Anne spotted Jim talking to a bald, heavyset man. Jim looked exhausted and Mrs. Hawthorne had disappeared. Some wife she was! Why didn't she see that he was taken care of? Didn't she have any concern for him at all? Anne walked slowly across the room, unwilling to interrupt his conversation but worried that he might be overdoing things.

She stood beside him and put her hand on his

shoulder. He looked up and his face brightened as he covered her hand with his and spoke to the man beside him. "George, have you met Anne?"

The man rose and nodded. "I certainly have met your charming daughter-in-law."

Anne recognized him then as Dr. George Koenig, the Hawthorne family physician. She smiled and spoke. "I'm sorry, doctor, I didn't recognize you at first or I wouldn't have intruded. I was worried that Ji—Dad—might be getting tired." She wasn't sure it would be proper to call her supposed father-in-law Jim to his friends.

Jim squeezed her hand, and Dr. Koenig looked at him with envy. "I hope you appreciate this young lady, Jim. She's not only beautiful but compassionate as well. I have a lot of patients who would give anything to have someone who was so worried about them."

The sadness returned to Jim's expression as he nodded. "How well I know. Rory showed a lot more sense than any of the rest of the family did when he married Anne. I'm so glad he had her this past year."

Jim's voice broke and he looked away, trying to bring his unstable emotions under control. Dr. Koenig looked at Anne and murmured softly, "See to it he's put to bed immediately. He's had all he can stand for one day."

At first Jim protested that it would be impolite for him to leave, but Anne promised to bring lunch for two on a tray as soon as Wolf had him comfortably ensconced in bed and he finally agreed.

It was while Anne was filling a tray with food that

Matt appeared again. He looked grim as he said, "Your grief doesn't seem to have taken the edge off your appetite. Are you planning to eat all that?"

She shrank from the hurt his biting words inflicted, but she wasn't going to let him intimidate her. "I'm having lunch with Jim, in his room."

Matt looked around, surprised. "Is something wrong? Why is Dad in his room?"

"Because he was tired and upset and you and your mother didn't even seem to notice!" she flared. "The doctor told me to see that he was put to bed immediately."

Matt looked at his watch and swore. "I didn't realize it was so late." He met her accusing stare. "That's the second crack you've made today about my mother. I gather you don't approve of her?"

Now that Anne had gotten started, she found it impossible to tone down her anger. "I don't presume to judge her on anything else, but yes, I think it's terrible the way she neglects her husband. What kind of marriage do they have?"

Matt didn't raise his voice. "Did it ever occur to you that he might want it that way?"

"Never," she retorted. "No man wants to cuddle up to an iceberg!"

Again Matt's voice held no emotion. "He doesn't cuddle up to her. They've had separate rooms for ten years. He was the one who moved across the hall."

Anne knew she should shut up, but her temper got the best of her. "No doubt he had good reason. Besides, no matter how things were before his stroke, now he needs love and warmth and emotional support."

Matt eyed her with disdain. "And you feel you're just the person to give it to him?"

Anne gasped at the suddeness of his attack, but before she could say anything further, Polly Parker joined them. She slipped an arm through Matt's and said, "Hey, you two, tone it down. If you must quarrel, can't you find someplace less public?" Her look told Anne that Polly was delighted that Anne and Matt were quarreling.

Matt ignored Polly and pulled his arm free to pick up the tray Anne had been filling. "If you're ready with this," he said through clenched teeth, "I'll carry it upstairs for you."

"You needn't bother—" she started to say, but he had gone ahead of her and she had to hurry to catch up. They left Polly standing there, staring after them.

Wolf had finished putting Jim to bed and was on his way out when Matt and Anne arrived. Jim looked pale and exhausted, propped up against the colorful sheets and pillowcases on the wide bed.

Anne had never been in Jim's room before. She hadn't even known which one was his until now. It was at the other end of the hall from hers; and, to her surprise, he had a suite, consisting of two rooms, a booklined study furnished with a large walnut desk, a leather couch and several upholstered chairs, and a bedroom with a private bath. As in the den downstairs, Jim's rooms were furnished in heavy, masculine furniture built for comfort and wear. There were no antiques in sight.

Jim greeted them and Matt busied himself arranging food on a bed tray, which he set up across Jim's

82

lap. When he finished, he straightened and asked, "Do you need help, Dad?"

Jim grunted. "I've been feeding myself for a long time."

Matt nodded. "I know, I just thought—well, if you're okay I'll go back downstairs and try to get rid of the last of that crowd." He glanced at Anne. "Don't stay long. As soon as you've finished eating you'd better come back downstairs and let Dad rest."

Jim's fork stopped in midair. "When *I* want her to go, *I'll* tell her so."

Matt grimaced and caught Anne's eye, gesturing that he wanted her to follow him to the door. When they got there he said quietly, "I'd advise you not to climb into bed with him."

Anne's eyes flashed with fury, but she could only stare speechlessly at him until he turned to go.

It was less than an hour later that Anne was once again downstairs, carrying the tray of dirty dishes to the kitchen. She hadn't been in the kitchen wing before, but she found it without too much trouble. There was a kitchen, a laundry, a pantry, a huge closet for cleaning supplies and a bathroom. Bess had mentioned once that the servants' quarters were above the four-car garage. Such an enormous house! She'd been there almost a week and still hadn't seen it all.

The right side of the house seemed deserted. Apparently Matt had done as he said he would and cleared out the last of the visitors. Mrs. Hawthorne had probably gone to her room. She certainly hadn't stopped in to see how her husband was faring. Anne felt only contempt for the woman, but she wished she hadn't been quite so vocal about it earlier with Matt. After all, the woman was his mother, and he knew her better than Anne did. Maybe she did have some redeeming qualities, but for the life of her Anne couldn't think of any.

She sighed and walked through the empty drawing room. Now that the pressure was off and the strain that had kept her going all day had lessened, she felt the vitality drain from her and her legs trembled with weakness. She had no intention of trying to relax in the empty, cavernous drawing room, but Jim had told her she could use the den anytime she wanted. It was cozy and intimate and she knew there would be a warm fire in the fireplace. She would curl up on the sofa and watch the TV news.

She walked across the hall and soundlessly opened the door. The room was dim, the only light a lamp in the corner and the glow from the fire. She'd started into the room before she saw the two figures by the window, twined so closely as to look like one. Anne gasped and started to retreat as a dark head raised and looked right at her. It was Matt, and his chocolate eyes riveted hers with a look of sardonic disdain as he once more lowered his head to Polly's upturned mouth.

Anne turned and fled to her room.

Hours later, she was propped up with large, luxurious pillows in her bed, reading, when there was a knock on the door. Before she had a chance to answer, it opened, and Matt, dressed only in slacks and a shirt opened down the front, walked in. Anne glared and said, "This is the second time you've burst in here without being invited. Aren't I allowed any privacy?"

Matt walked over and dropped down on the other side of her double bed and stretched out full length on his back beside her. She watched, incredulous, as he said, "Oh, don't be ridiculous, Anne. We've already spent a night together, and, as I remember, you even invited me to stay after I offered to leave." There was mockery in his voice as he spoke.

She gasped. "That was different and you know it!"

He put his forearm over his eyes and groaned. "I just came in to see how you were, so for heaven's sake don't scold. Actually, you look fine, but *I'm* tired."

A twinge of sympathy stirred in her. Matt was so strong and self-sufficient that she'd almost forgotten he was grieving too. Rory had been his only brother, the baby, born when Matt was eight years old. Anne had been aware of his pain when he first came to claim her in the hospital in Nebraska, but since coming to Denver he had been so disagreeable to her that she'd forgotten he was hurting too.

She reached over with her unbound arm and stroked his head. He lay quietly as she caressed him gently with her fingers and said, "After that scene I saw building up in the den, I'd think you'd be content and relaxed by now."

He laughed mockingly. "Oh, sure. Polly and I made love on the floor in plain sight of any of the servants who happened to wander by. Next time we're going to charge admission!"

She felt an overwhelming sense of relief. If he'd

just denied it she wouldn't have believed him, but put like that she could see how absurd it was. She grinned and said, "Okay, so I jumped to conclusions, but you do have a bedroom and I won't believe it if you tell me she refused to spend the night with you."

He shrugged, careful not to dislodge her fingers. "She probably would have if I'd asked her to, but I didn't."

For the first time that day Anne felt happy. It was none of her business whether he made love to Polly or not, but his admission that he hadn't even asked her brought a feeling of joy. Her fingers trailed down his cheek and lightly massaged the tight muscles in his neck as she asked, "What is it you want of me, Matt?"

He shivered as her massaging fingers worked around to his nape. "I want some of the tender loving care you've been lavishing on Dad all day." His voice was cold and hard again; the brief moment of companionship they'd shared was gone.

All the happiness and joy were driven away as she jerked her hand away and sat up straight. He moved his arm from across his eyes and looked at her, surprised, as she blazed at him, "I've had enough of your ugly accusations! Just get out of here and leave me alone!"

He calmly shrugged out of his shirt, rolled over on his stomach and put his head on his folded arms, ignoring her outburst. "Quit acting like an outraged virgin and rub my back. It aches all the way to my head."

She hesitated, then quietly resumed her left-handed massage. She wasn't going to quarrel with him; they were both too spent physically and emotionally for that. She lay back against the pillows and relaxed as her fingers sought the knotted muscles across his shoulders.

Anne had never had a man in bed with her before; Aunt Martha would have had hysterics if she'd only known. For that matter, Anne had never touched a man's body this way before. Matt's shoulders were wide, and she was aware of a pleasant, tingling sensation that ran from her fingertips, where they touched him, up her arm and exploded in pleasure points throughout her body. She wondered if her touch affected him the same way.

She knew she should put a stop to this and send him away, but her hand had a will of its own as it caressed his back, shoulders and neck. With a little sigh he began to relax, and before long his breathing became deep and regular and she knew he was asleep.

What was she going to do? He'd looked so exhausted when he came in and now he was sleeping like a baby. If she woke him and sent him to his own room, he'd probably have trouble falling asleep again. What harm could it do to let him sleep here? He needed the rest so badly and she'd be sure to get him up and out of there in the morning. She'd get up in a minute herself, and sleep in a chair. But just for now it felt so nice to be here; she'd just rest for a few minutes first. She turned off the lamp and snuggled down in the bed beside him.

It didn't work out quite the way she'd planned. Sometime during the night she half woke to find herself cradled in Matt's sinewy arms, his lips nuzzling the sensitive hollows of her neck. Instinctively she cuddled closer and his hold tightened. The mat of curly black hair on his chest was rough against the softness of her skin, and a rush of warmth flooded through her. She liked the feel of his half-nude body against her, his hand brushing the side of her breast. He lifted his head and his mouth covered hers, gently probing until her lips parted in a gesture of surrender.

By now she was wide awake and receiving urgent messages from her mind to stop him, but her body wouldn't cooperate. A nagging little doubt nudged her and she twisted her head away and murmured, "Matt, I'm not Polly."

He trailed kisses down her throat and buried his face between her breasts as he growled, "I know who you are, Anne; I just wish you weren't such a lying, deceiving little sorceress."

It was like lightning! It happened so fast that it was a minute before she realized she'd been struck. His words, spoken under such tender and intimate circumstances, came as a shocking, jolting, ripping surprise. The fingers that had been stroking him tightened around a fistful of hair and she pulled before pushing him away with all her strength.

He cried out with pain and loosened his hold on her just enough to allow her to jump off the bed, sending him sprawling across it. She turned on the light as he looked up at her, his eyes wide and his mouth open. "You little wildcat! What's wrong with you? Come back here!"

She stood facing him, fire in her eyes. "Get out of

here, Matt! Get out of here and don't ever touch me again! You're really something. You come to me for comfort and then treat me like a—a lady of pleasure!"

Her voice broke and she turned away so he wouldn't see her anguish. He scrambled off the bed and stood behind her, his voice grim.

"But that's what you are, Angela, although there *is* a better word for it. You sold yourself to Rory. You went to bed with him once to let him sample the merchandise and then teased him without putting out until he had to have you whatever the cost. The price was marriage and an unlimited charge account. You forget that Rory and I were very close. He confided in me when he had problems, and he had plenty of them with you."

Stunned, Anne turned to face him, her mouth open to protest, but he didn't give her a chance. "Oh, sure, you were sweet and willing enough as long as he let you have what you wanted. You spent money like it grew on trees. Remember, I paid the bills."

He walked away and started putting on his shirt. "You're a talented actress, I'll give you that. Once or twice you even had me believing your poor, frightened little-girl act, but, true to form, you finally overplayed it. All that tender, loving concern for Dad today was an inspiration. You've got him eating out of your hand, but you forgot something, little sister. You forgot to cry. Not once, all day long, have you shed a tear for Rory. You forgot that widows are expected to grieve!"

Anne stood frozen. She knew the blood had

drained from her face and her eyes were round with horror, but she couldn't move or speak. It was like being entombed in ice; she could see and hear but she couldn't respond. Matt finished buttoning his shirt, and, without turning around, he unfastened his pants so he could tuck his shirt in, then zipped them up again. It was a deliberate gesture of disrespect and Anne felt like the expensive prostitute he accused her of being.

She struggled desperately to get herself under control, to say something. To at least make an excuse for not crying. At last a sound, like the whimper of a wounded puppy, forced itself from her throat and she whispered, "Everyone grieves in a different manner."

He shrugged. "That's true. It might even be an acceptable answer—if you'll answer just one question."

Anne nodded her head slowly. "All right."

His face was like granite and his eyes like ice. "What happened to the baby, Angela? Your baby—and Rory's?"

Chapter Five

Baby! What baby! Oh, no! Did Rory and Angela have a baby hidden away somewhere?

The room tilted and Anne clutched the high bedpost with her good arm in an effort to steady herself. No, that wasn't possible. If Angela and Rory had a child who had been left in someone else's care, Matt would have asked her about it the moment she regained consciousness. Was Angela pregnant? Neither she nor Rory had mentioned it if she was.

Anne's knees trembled as she continued to clutch the bedpost for support. Matt apparently mistook her shock for surprise and said, "You didn't think I knew about the baby, did you? Didn't Rory tell you he'd written to me?"

Her wide brown eyes stared at him as he continued. "The first letter was written a couple of months ago, after one of your numerous quarrels. He said you didn't care for him, only the family name and money, and he was seriously considering a divorce."

Anne continued to stare, unable to speak as he jammed his hands into his pockets and paced in front of her. "Then, three weeks ago, he wrote again saying you had just discovered you were pregnant and things were better between the two of you. He was going to give the marriage another chance for the sake of the baby."

He stopped his pacing and his hand shot out to grip her chin and force her head up so her eyes met his. The loathing that burned from his dark eyes shriveled her as he grated, "You lying little witch! The first thing I asked the doctor when I got to the hospital was if the baby had survived the accident. He didn't know what I was talking about. He said you weren't then and never had been pregnant! You deliberately lied to Rory so he wouldn't divorce you! You counted on the unbridled physical attraction he felt for you to get you pregnant in a hurry so he wouldn't know of your deception."

He gave her head a vicious twist before dropping his hand. His eyes raked over her body, undressing her, leaving her naked and unprotected from his gaze as he sneered, "You make me sick!" and stormed out of the room, slamming the door behind him.

His rage had been a tangible thing, holding her together with its intensity. When it was removed she slid slowly down the bedpost and landed in a broken, sobbing heap on the floor.

It was a long night. When Anne finally pulled

herself together enough to get up off the floor and into bed, she was cold and stiff and exhausted, but she couldn't sleep. Matt's face swam before her, twisted with hate, and his accusations beat in her brain until her head throbbed. She couldn't blame him; he had every right to hate Angela if she made Rory as miserable as he indicated to Matt. Was Angela really pregnant? Or had she lied to Rory as Matt had accused? Anne was inclined to think not. A wife would be a fool to attempt that kind of deception. Angela was streetwise and she would have known that. No, there had apparently been three deaths that dreadful day: Rory, Angela and their unborn child. But she couldn't tell that to Matt without revealing her own deception.

Anne shifted restlessly and ground her teeth in frustration when the heavy cast made turning difficult. Matt apparently hadn't told Constance and James about the baby. Rory and Angela were probably going to make that announcement when they got home. Why did everything have to be so complicated? If she ever got out of this mess she'd never lie again!

She shifted again, dragging the cast with her. Her thoughts kept returning to Matt. No wonder he had been so resentful, so distrustful of her. And still he had moments of tenderness. He'd been gentle and concerned when she was in the hospital, and on the way to Denver he'd held her and reassured her when her fear of meeting his parents became unbearable. Tonight he'd sent Polly home and come to her for comfort and she'd been glad. She'd wanted to hold him, caress him and give him the loving he so desperately needed. But that wasn't possible. She couldn't love Matt! It would destroy her completely!

Anne got out of bed when the light began to filter through the closed draperies. The face that looked back at her from the mirror as she washed and brushed her teeth was older, more mature, than it had been two weeks ago. It was thinner, sharper with the memory of physical pain. The fading bruises were more noticable this morning because the rosy glow of youthful good health had been replaced with the pale, drawn pallor of lost sleep and stolen illusions. The pain that looked out of her eyes was not physical but composed of shock and hurt and horror. What could she say to Matt? She had no defense against his accusations, no way to protect herself from the torment he seemed intent on inflicting.

She struggled into a pair of designer jeans and grimaced as she remembered fingering a pair of these same jeans at a store in Chicago. She'd been shocked at the price, but now she had a whole rack of them in various colors, thanks to Angela and her extravagance.

She couldn't manage a bra but found a hot pink velour sweatshirt with deep sleeves that went over her cast. She painstakingly pulled it over her head with her left arm. She was determined to learn to dress herself even if she couldn't use her right arm. It didn't pay to be dependent on anyone; they always let you down.

She walked softly on the stairs. It was very early and she was sure nobody was up yet as she walked diagonally across the entryway and down the hall on the left to the small, sunny room beside the kitchen. The breakfast room was one of her favorite places. Unlike the coldly formal dining room, this room was bright, cheerful and intimate, with its buttercup yellow decor and the fresh flower arrangement of gold, brown and rust pompom chrysanthemums backed with green leaves.

She was so intent on her thoughts that she'd taken several steps into the room before she realized she wasn't alone. Matt was sitting at the round, linen-covered table with a cup of coffee and the morning paper. She caught her breath. Matt was the last person she wanted to see. She couldn't possibly face him yet. If he lashed out at her, or demanded explanations, she'd come unglued again.

She started to back out quietly, but his stern voice commanded. "Come on in and have some breakfast. Coffee and food are on the serving table."

She was caught! She knew he would make a scene if she tried to leave. She averted her eyes as she walked across the room and poured herself a cup of coffee. She carried it to the table and took a seat as far from Matt as possible, but it wasn't far enough. He could easily reach out and touch her. For the first time since she'd been in the Hawthorne home, she wished they were eating at the big table in the dining room. In there she wouldn't be close enough to him to smell the familiar shaving lotion, to hear his every breath.

Matt didn't look up from his paper or speak again, and she took a sip of her coffee as her undisciplined, hurt-filled eyes peeked at him through thick lashes. His face had a look of unutterable weariness and she knew he hadn't slept either.

What could she possibly say to him? Her throat felt tight and full of tears. Would he ask her to leave? It seemed likely, but if he did, where would she go? How could she support herself with her arm in a cast this way? It wouldn't even help now if she told him the truth. He'd be just as angry with her for deceiving him and his parents as he was with Angela for deceiving Rory. It was probably a crime to masquerade as somebody else, and Matt wouldn't hesitate to turn her over to the authorities. She shivered as she thought of it.

Matt looked up, almost as if he had felt her shiver, and frowned. "I told you to eat breakfast."

She shook her head. "I—I'm not hungry."

With a mild oath he threw down his paper and went over to the serving table, where he took a plate and filled it high with ham, scrambled eggs, hot biscuits and slices of fruit. He brought it back to the table and set it in front of her as he snarled, "Now, eat!"

She picked up her fork and speared a small portion of eggs. The smell of them made her stomach turn over and she laid the fork down again and stood up. She couldn't sit there across from Matt and calmly eat breakfast!

She wandered over to the window and stood looking out. It hadn't snowed in several days, and this morning the sky was clear. In a short while the sun would come out and maybe it would warm up a little. Except for the funeral yesterday, she hadn't been away from the house since Matt brought her here. She was gaining in strength every day and soon she would have to get out and find a job. Then she could tell the Hawthornes the truth about herself and leave. And hope they wouldn't put her in jail.

A voice beside her broke into her reverie. "Anne, your breakfast is getting cold."

She jumped, and when she saw Matt's arm extended toward her she cringed and a wordless "don't" formed on her lips. An expression of—remorse?—no, it couldn't be—twisted Matt's face as he barked, "I'm not going to hit you, you know!"

She hung her head and whispered, "I'm sorry."

The palms of his hands circled either side of her face and lifted her head to look at him. His gaze missed nothing as it traveled over her dainty features and his thumbs traced the blue shadows under her fright-filled eyes.

With a little groan he murmured, "You look at me like I'm some kind of monster. Last night every word I hurled at you made you wince, as though they were delivered on the cutting edge of a whip. I could almost see them biting into you. Honestly, Angela, I—"

His hands dropped from her face and he turned and walked out of the room.

Anne stood there for a moment, her tattered nerves screaming with frustration. She was torn by Matt's anguish, his inability to fit Anne into Angela's mold. If only she could tell him the truth and rely on his ability to understand her motives and forgive. But that wasn't possible. Matt's background was too different from hers. He'd always been rich, secure and loved, all the things Anne had never known. How could she explain to him the lonliness, the emptiness, the fear that had haunted her almost ever since she could remember.

Matt had always had family, social position, prestige. He was the type who wrote a generous tax-deductible check to the United Charities once a year and considered he'd done his duty to the underprivileged. No need to actually wallow in their misery with them!

Suddenly Anne couldn't bear the Hawthornes or their house any longer. Without a second look at the breakfast growing cold on the plate, she hurried upstairs to her room and pulled the fake fur cape over her shoulders. She took a five-dollar bill and some change from Angela's purse and stuffed them into her pocket. She'd learned in Chicago not to walk around with a purse if you didn't want it snatched.

The sun was just coming up as she shut the heavy front door behind her and stepped out into the cold, brisk, winter air. She walked down the half-circle driveway and turned to the right.

Thank heaven she'd gotten out of the house without anyone seeing her. She didn't know where Matt had gone, but the rest of the household was obviously still in bed. It was very early, and although there was no wind, the air was icy. She could see her breath, and she was glad she'd found the heavy-knit red and white stocking cap and mittens or her hands and ears would have frozen. It would have been better if she'd remembered to wear boots, but the thick-soled shoes she had on would be all right as long as it didn't thaw too much, which was hardly likely in this cold.

A picture of Matt the first time she'd seen him formed in her mind. Those deep, chocolate-brown eyes had been filled with compassion as he bent over her hospital bed. His nose was just the right size for the square face and his mouth was strictly masculine but with a sensual vulnerability that could promise paradise when he smiled and bring down the wrath of Hades with a frown.

His manner that day had been kind, even tender, as he folded her small hand into his big one and held it while she slept. He'd known everything about Angela then that he did now, and still he had treated her with gentleness and concern. She'd been badly injured and he'd thought she'd lost her husband; he'd put aside his animosity and dislike and treated her with the loving respect reserved for someone special.

Anne sighed. It must have been then that she fell in love with him. There was no use trying to hide it from herself; it was no longer possible. She loved this man who thought she was Angela and hated her so violently. But was it really hate? He'd soothed her, protected her, seen she had everything she needed, and last night he had come to her for comfort. He thought she was the selfish, greedy woman who had made his young brother's life such torture, and still he'd sent Polly Parker away and come to her, Anne, for solace in his grief and pain over Rory.

Anne closed her eyes as a wave of anguish rolled over her. If only he'd kept his mouth shut and let events take their natural course. She could admit now that if he'd given in to his need for her, and not lashed out at her, she would have let him make love to her. She couldn't have denied him, or herself.

She shivered, not with cold but with longing. This morning Matt had let her see the torment his confused feelings were causing him. His bitterness was for Angela, his tenderness for Anne, but he didn't know they were two separate people, and she couldn't tell him. She didn't dare tell him the whole story, because then his bitterness and distrust would be for Anne, and she couldn't stand that.

The sound of childish voices shouting at one another brought her back to the present and she looked around her, bewildered at the change of scenery. This neighborhood was nothing like the one she'd just come from. The houses were smaller and set closer together, and there were bundled up children frolicking in the snow. There was also a sprinkling of businesses, a supermarket on one corner, a gas station on the other, and to her right, halfway up the intersecting street, was a doughnut shop.

Anne realized that she was tired and hungry. She'd left her breakfast uneaten and she must have been walking for a long time. Her legs were weak with fatigue. This was the first time she'd walked further than from one room to another since she got out of the hospital, and she was afraid if she didn't sit down she'd fall down.

She turned and trudged up the slight incline to the doughnut shop. It was warm inside and the smell of fresh, yeasty dough made her mouth water. She ordered a cup of coffee and a glazed doughnut and went over to one of the small tables by the window. She sank wearily into the chair and unbuttoned her fur cape as she settled back and took a sip of the hot, fragrant coffee.

The hands of the clock on the wall pointed to ten o'clock. She'd been walking for at least two hours. No wonder she was tired. She'd sit there in the warm friendly room for awhile until she was rested, and then retrace her steps back to the Hawthorne house.

She got a refill on her coffee and sat watching the people go by outside the window until ten-thirty, when she got up and started home.

She was momentarily confused when she came out of the doughnut shop, but then she turned right and quickened her pace. She wished she'd watched where she was going earlier. After several blocks the area seemed to be getting worse instead of better. She spotted a bus stopping a few feet ahead of her. Surely the bus would go right past the Hawthornes' home? She ran to catch it and climbed aboard.

She dug in the pocket of her fancy jeans for the proper change and sat down next to a window. The bus was warm and the seats comfortable and she leaned back with a sigh as her thoughts returned to Matt.

Anne knew now that it would be impossible for her to stay with the Hawthornes any longer. She couldn't stand the tension that existed between her and Matt. It would just get worse until it exploded in some nameless way that would do violence to them all, and Jim must be protected. His health was too precarious to withstand a family fight.

No, she had to leave, and the sooner the better. She still had some money, not much, but maybe it would buy a bus ticket to California. She'd tell Matt and his parents that she'd decided to go back to Cambridge where her friends were. They'd never know she'd actually gone in the other direction.

A tap on the shoulder brought her abruptly back to the present and she looked up into the face of the bus driver. He frowned as he said, "We're at the end of the line, lady. You'll have to get off."

Startled, Anne looked out the window. The neighborhood was decidedly seedy, with rundown shacks, unpaved roads and no sidewalks. Where on earth was she? She asked the driver and he gave her a look of disgust as he told her the address. It meant nothing to her but the driver was impatiently nudging her toward the door.

She got off the bus and looked around. There were a couple of ragged children playing in the street, and an elderly woman in a shapeless, dirty coat and torn headscarf shuffled along the edge of the road muttering to herself.

Anne shivered and started to walk briskly. She'd have to find a telephone and look up the Hawthornes' address. It hadn't occurred to her to find out what it was and write it down before she started out this morning.

She walked several blocks down the road before

she came to a gas station with a phone booth. She pulled off her mittens and turned to the H's in the phone book. There weren't many *Hawthornes* listed and none was either *James* or *Matthew*. They must have an unlisted phone number. It was silly of her not to have thought of it. All rich people had unlisted phone numbers, didn't they?

She slumped down on the small padded stool. Now what was she going to do? She'd managed to get herself thoroughly lost and didn't even know the address or phone number of the place she was staying. How could she have been so stupid? She'd started out for a walk around the block and ended up miles away with no idea of where she was or where she came from.

She looked up as a police car drove up and parked at the gas pumps. The police! She could ask them for Jim's address. Surely they could help her. She opened the door of the telephone booth and walked over to the policeman, who was pumping gas into the car.

He looked up as she approached and she said, "Excuse me, I seem to be lost. Do you know where Mr. James Hawthorne lives? He's a well-known businessman here in Denver."

The policeman surveyed her briefly as he answered, "Why do you want to know where James Hawthorne lives?"

Anne didn't like his manner and answered crisply, "I'm staying there."

The policeman's scrutiny was longer this time. "Then how come you don't know the address?"

She could see it wasn't going to be easy to explain. "I—I've only been there a short time and I didn't ask the address. I went out for a walk this morning and got lost, and now I don't know how to get back to the house."

The gas pump kicked off and the policeman hung the hose back on the tank before he spoke. "Who are you, lady? Do you have any identification?"

Anne was beginning to be frightened. Why couldn't the policeman just tell her what she wanted to know and stop this questioning? She drew herself up and tried to sound dignified. "I'm Angela Hawthorne, James Hawthorne's daughter-in-law."

The policeman fitted the top back on the gas tank. "If you're his daughter-in-law, how come you don't know his address? Let me see your identification."

Anne's fear was increasing. What had she gotten herself into? Why couldn't the man just answer her question and leave her alone? She shifted position and said, "I didn't bring my purse when I left the house this morning. I was only going for a short walk, but I must have taken a wrong turn somewhere." She reached into her jeans pocket and took out the five-dollar bill. "This is all I've got with me. I didn't bring a billfold."

The policeman's eyes narrowed as he continued to watch her. "Look, doll, you're miles away from the Hawthornes'. If Mr. Hawthorne sent for you and you lost the address, I can't help you."

"Sent for me?" Anne questioned. "Why would he send for me? I live in his house."

The policeman's face was inscrutable. "Okay,

have it your way, but it wouldn't be the first time a girl was called to a rich guy's apartment and couldn't find the address." He walked to the car door on the passenger side and opened it. "Get in, I'll drive you to the station and check out your story." His look was ominous. "It better be true."

It wasn't until he'd started the car that she understood what he'd been implying. He thought she was a call girl!

Anne had never been so humiliated. She sat stiffly in her seat and looked straight ahead all the way to the police station. Once there, she was questioned further, and finally one of the officers put through a call to the Hawthorne residence. When he came back, he looked decidedly uneasy.

He smiled weakly and said, "Sorry, Mrs. Hawthorne, but your in-laws don't give out their address and phone number to the general public and it's our duty to protect them. I hope you understand." Anne nodded, relieved, and he continued. "I spoke to Matthew Hawthorne and he said he'd be right down."

Oh, no, not that! Why did they have to disturb Matt? Why couldn't they just have given her the address once they knew who she was and let her take a cab home? She looked at the clock on the wall. One twenty-five. No wonder she was so tired; she'd been wandering around for almost six hours. One of the policewomen brought her a cup of coffee and she settled back in her chair to wait.

It was forty minutes before Matt came through the door, accompanied by a squat, sandy-haired man in a business suit. Matt looked straight at Anne, and there was no misreading that look—he was furious! His voice was soft, too soft, as he said, "Are you all right, Anne?"

She nodded, and he introduced the other man as the chief of police. The chief looked worried as he hurried to apologize. "Mrs. Hawthorne, I can't tell you how sorry I am that you were put through an interrogation. We were only trying to protect your family from an intruder. I hope you understand."

Again Anne nodded and then stood as Matt put his hand under the elbow of her broken arm and said, "Have you any complaints about the way you were treated?"

All she wanted was to get out of there. She shook her head and answered, "No, the officers were very considerate."

Well, it was half true. They had fallen all over themselves to be nice to her once they found out she really was a member of the Hawthorne family. She certainly couldn't tell Matt the first officer had mistaken her for a call girl. After all, so had Matt!

He helped her into her cape and escorted her to the car without a word. Once inside, however, his voice was fiery with rage as he snapped, "I suppose your idea was to punish me by running off and making me worry about what had happened to you. Well, you'll be happy to know it worked. You scared the daylights out of me; but you might have given at least a passing thought to what your nasty little scheme would do to Dad. He's been frantic! He insisted on driving all over town with me to look for you, and now his blood pressure has shot up out of control. He's in real danger of having another stroke."

Jim! Oh, no! It had never occurred to her that anyone would worry about her being gone. She gasped, but before she could say anything Matt was slashing at her with words again.

"You selfish little idiot! Don't you ever think of anyone but yourself? You're the one who's been playing up to Dad, showing all that tender concern, making him dependent on you for the emotional support he doesn't get from Mother. Well, this time you really boxed yourself in. His health is extremely precarious. His blood pressure is unstable at best, and when he's upset, it goes sky-high. He could have another stroke at any time, and if he does, it will probably kill him. I don't intend to let you bring that about."

Anne wondered how much more of this she could stand. Matt's words were lacerating her very soul! How could he possibly think she would deliberately endanger Jim's life? Jim, whom she loved as a father. She had to try to make Matt understand that she hadn't done what he thought. She twisted her fingers together and said, "Matt, please, you don't understand. At least give me a chance to explain."

His knuckles whitened as his hands gripped the steering wheel. "Oh, you've had plenty of time to come up with several believable explanations, but you can save your breath. I don't intend to waste my time listening to them. You're going to listen to me for a change. I don't know what kind of magic you worked on Dad, but he thinks you're some kind of angel and he's become dangerously attached to you.

You literally hold his life in those two grasping little hands of yours. He's more vulnerable to you now than to any of us."

Anne felt that she must either speak or explode, but before she could get a word out he raged on. "You deliberately fostered his dependence on you, and now you're going to cater to it. I'm going to see to it that you give him all the loving care he needs for as long as he needs it. You're going to be the most devoted daughter a man ever had, and the operative word is *daughter*. If I catch you sleeping with him again, I'll—"

Anne's head jerked up, indignation written in every line of her countenance. It was at that moment that they both saw the car a few yards ahead of them braking for a stop sign on the quiet, residential street. Matt's foot hit the brake and he swerved toward the curb in an effort to avoid hitting the stopped car. Anne, who had forgotten to fasten her seat belt, was thrown against the dash and onto the floor of the car.

Matt swore viciously as he moved to the middle of the front seat and picked her up from the floor. He clutched her tightly to him, and she could feel him tremble as he demanded, "Anne! Oh, Anne, are you hurt? Did you hit your arm?"

Anne was dazed from the suddenness of the jolt, and her head hurt where she'd bumped it against the dash, but it wasn't the pain she was thinking of. It was the concern in Matt's voice, the pressure of his arms about her. Did it really matter that much to him if she was injured?

He murmured apologies and endearments as his

hands and lips caressed her, and she snuggled into his arms as she said, "I'm all right, just a little shook up."

His arms cradled her, but his voice was suddenly harsh as he grated, "You're driving me right out of my mind. You look and act so young and innocent and vulnerable, but I know my brother. Rory wouldn't lie to me, and all his letters talked about a grasping, scheming little tramp who tormented him till he married her and then made life miserable for him with her demands and her indifference. You're not going to do the same thing to me."

Anne tipped her head back and looked up into dark eyes filled with a painful confusion. His face was pale, and there were lines of anxiety in his broad forehead. She raised the fingers of her left hand to his lips and he kissed them as, with a little groan, his mouth descended to hers and clung. She slid her hand along his neck until it became entangled in his ebony hair.

She felt Matt's muscles tense with the effort to keep the kiss light, but it was a losing battle. The gentleness turned to hunger and the hunger to fire. His hands pulled her to him, molding her to the hard male contours of him until their heavy clothing became an unbearable frustration. He unfastened her cape while she unzipped the parka he wore with his denim slacks.

Now confined only by her shirt, her breasts rubbed against his firm muscular chest and a tremor shook him as his tongue forced her lips apart and explored the moistness of her mouth.

All good sense and self-discipline deserted Anne,

leaving only the aching need to be possessed that only Matt could assuage. His restless hand slid down her jean-clad hip and rested on her thigh. Without conscious thought she twined her leg with his in an effort to get even closer to him. The sensuous movement snapped his tenuous control and he twisted so his body covered hers, pinning her against the cushion, his mouth ravishing hers, unable to stop.

And then he did stop, pushing her away from him with a strangled groan. He drew a shaky breath and gathered her into his arms again as he settled her back in the seat. He was trembling with the searing passion that had almost been their undoing, and he rubbed his cheek against her disheveled hair as he said, "I apologize. I never lost control like that before."

Anne blushed. It wasn't all his fault; she'd responded without a murmur of protest. She'd never felt anything like this before, and she knew Matt was the only man who could start that kind of fire in her. She had to make him understand that she was not what she seemed.

She put her left hand up to caress his rough cheek and murmured, "Trust me, Matt; I won't hurt you, I swear."

He stiffened and his hands fastened on her arms, pushing her away from him. She watched, confused, as the lingering desire in his eyes turned to ice and his mouth twisted into an ugly sneer as he taunted, "You're right; you won't, because you're not going to get the chance. And while we're on the subject, we just buried your husband yesterday. Don't you think you should wait until the flowers wilt on his grave before you start in on me?"

Anne stared in horror as she flung herself to the other side of the car. She'd forgotten about Rory! But Matt hadn't. Rory was his brother and he thought Anne was Rory's wife. How he must hate her!

Chapter Six

Matt and Anne drove the rest of the way home in strained silence. When they pulled up in the driveway, Matt got out of the car and disappeared inside the house. Anne sat there, trying to pull herself together. This whole situation was impossible. She couldn't live with Matt's ambivalence, hating her one moment, passionately involved with her the next. No one could stand that for long, but neither could she leave. If she did it would upset Jim and might precipitate another stroke.

She rested her head against the closed window and took a deep breath. She would have been better off to have stayed in Chicago and taken a firm stand against Aunt Martha and Clarence. Never again would she envy rich people. Living in luxury didn't guarantee happiness.

Because she didn't have a key, she had to ring to gain admittance to the house. The door was opened by Wolf, whose expression changed from surprise to consternation. "Mrs. Rory! I thought you came in with Mr. Matt." His eyes narrowed as he looked at her. "What's wrong with you?"

She felt his hard, comforting arm around her as she realized that either she or the room was swaying. Wolf scooped her up easily in his powerful arms. She was shivering with weakness.

He headed for the staircase as she protested feebly, "Put me down, Wolf. I can walk."

He paid no attention but continued up the stairs. At the top they met Matt coming down the hall from the direction of his room. He looked startled but didn't raise his voice as he said, "What's going on?"

Wolf glared back at him. "That's what I'd like to know. Why did you leave the poor child outside by herself? When I opened the door for her she nearly fell at my feet."

He turned abruptly away from Matt and carried Anne to her room. Matt, who had followed them, opened the door and pulled back the covers on the bed so Wolf could set her down. When Wolf straightened up, Matt said, "Go downstairs and get her a sandwich and a glass of milk."

Wolf hesitated a minute, but a look from Matt sent him out the door. Matt showed no sympathy or concern as he sat on the side of the bed and began to slip off her shoes and socks. She drew up her legs in protest. "No, don't! I have to talk to Jim."

Matt jerked her legs down and continued removing her shoes. "Dad's asleep. Wolf gave him a heavy tranquilizer, so he'll sleep for several hours. You can talk to him at dinner."

113

Before she realized his intent, he had pulled apart the snap on her jeans and unzipped them. She twisted away. "Matt, stop that! Send Bess up; she'll help me undress."

He pulled her back toward him and began peeling off the tight jeans. His voice was expressionless as he said, "Shut up and lie still. You don't have anything I haven't seen before."

He tossed the jeans across the bottom of the bed and sat her up as he maneuvered her cast out of the pink velour sweat shirt, leaving her nude except for about six inches of bikini pantie that was more decorative than concealing.

He pushed her back against the pillows and asked where she kept her nightgowns. She pulled the sheet up to her chin as he rummaged through the drawer she indicated and came back with a black one that he slipped over her head and adjusted under the sheet.

He might as well have been dressing a mannequin for all the emotion he showed. How could he turn off so quickly? The touch of his hands on her bare skin left her nerves in shreds, but he was as cool and calm as though he were undressing a child. Less than an hour ago they had been welded together in a frenzy of uncontrollable passion, and now he was performing this intimate ritual without a tremor. The man was inhuman!

Bess came with a tray of food and Matt left without a word.

Anne slept deeply for three hours until she was wakened by Bess, who reminded her that dinner would be served in half an hour and that she still had to bathe and dress. Anne cursed herself for not leaving word to call her earlier; she wanted to talk to Jim before he went downstairs. With Bess's help she broke all speed records and drew her turquoise caftan over her head ten minutes ahead of schedule. The caftan brought out the touch of green in her brown eyes, and her only makeup was lipstick and eyebrow pencil.

Her turquoise-slippered feet raced along the corridor toward Jim's sitting room, where she knocked softly on the door. His hearty "Come in" boomed through to her and she entered. Jim was sitting in one of the lounge chairs in front of the fire. He was dressed for dinner and held out his right hand as he smiled at her. She took his hand and leaned over to kiss him on the cheek as he said, "You're looking lovely, my dear. Are you feeling all right now? You gave us quite a scare, disappearing that way."

Anne sank down on a small stool beside the chair. "I'm so sorry, Jim. It was such a stupid thing to do, getting lost that way. I went for a walk but didn't take my purse. Then I must have taken a wrong turn somewhere because I couldn't find my way back. I got on a bus that took me clear to the other side of the city. I felt like such an idiot when I couldn't identify myself to that policeman. He thought—"

Anne realized what she'd nearly said and clamped her mouth shut. Oh, heavens, why couldn't she think before she spoke?

Jim's curiosity had been provoked. "He thought what, Anne?"

She shook her head. "Oh, nothing."

He persisted. "Come on, tell me. What did he think?"

Anne knew he wasn't going to let her evade the question. "He—he thought I wanted to—to pester you about something," she lied.

Jim patted the top of her head absently. "I'm sorry you were treated like that, honey, but it's true that the police were only doing their job. The Hawthorne name and business are well known throughout the state, and we do get more than our share of cranks and crazies. I'd rather you didn't venture out alone. Wolf will take you anywhere you want to go."

She sighed. "I only wanted to go for a walk, Jim. I would have been all right if I'd paid more attention to where I was going."

"That's not the point. I don't want to scare you, Anne, but there's always a certain amount of danger that someone might decide to abduct you and hold you for ransom because you're a member of this family. Constance takes the necessary precautions and you must too. I'll get one of my security men to instruct you."

Anne stared at him, dumbfounded. "You've got to be kidding!" she exploded. "There's no one in the whole world who would pay ransom to get me back."

The idea was so ludicrous that she almost started to giggle. Imagine anyone thinking she was important enough to kidnap! Jim grinned down at her. "Oh, I don't know. I might be persuaded to pay a

116

dollar or two for you. You have a certain nuisance value."

His tone was light, but the look in his eyes told her how vulnerable he was where her safety was concerned. She caught her breath and knew if she tried to tell him how much his concern meant to her, she'd break down. Instead, she tried to match his lightness. "You don't fool me. You want me around because of my brilliant mind and breathtaking beauty."

He laughed. "And don't forget your nasty temper. If I didn't have you to browbeat me into eating properly and getting my rest, I might manage to live a peaceful life."

Suddenly they were both laughing as the intolerable strain of the past few hours evaporated. They were enjoying themselves immensely when a knock on the door interrupted them. Jim called, "Come in."

It was Matt, who came striding into the room. He stopped and looked from one grinning face to the other, puzzled. "What's so funny? I could hear you laughing clear down the hall."

Anne and Jim looked at each other and giggled again as Jim said, "Shall we tell him?"

Anne's laughter stopped. "No, Jim, please don't!"

Jim looked grimly from Anne to Matt but said nothing.

Matt's face darkened as he looked at them. "Mother sent me up to get you. We've been waiting dinner." He turned and left.

Even Matt's grim mood couldn't dampen Anne and Jim's mirth, and every time their glances met over the dinner table they broke into giggles. Matt glared and said nothing while Constance gave them all an account of the preparations being made to welcome the national head of one of the many clubs and committees she was involved with. As they lingered over custard pudding and coffee, Constance looked at Jim and asked, "What time did Robert Osborn say he'd be here?"

Jim looked at his gold wristwatch. "He should arrive any minute now." He put his napkin on the table. "We'd better go along to the library. Wolf will bring Robert in when he comes."

Anne hadn't known they were expecting visitors tonight, but she was glad of the excuse it gave her to go upstairs. She didn't think she could stand a whole evening in the same room with Matt. The air around them was charged with emotion, even if it was only disgust on his part. Ever since that fiery encounter between them earlier, she had been so sensitive to his every move that her nerves were quivering with tension.

As she rose from her chair, she said, "If you'll excuse me, I think I'll go to my room and read."

Constance shot her a quelling look and her voice was sharp as she snapped, "Please, Anne, don't be difficult. Robert is doing us a favor by coming here instead of making us go to his office, and I'm not going to let you pull another disappearing act. It's imperative that you be in on this meeting."

Anne's head shot up with surprise and she was aware that Matt had pushed back his chair and stood up as she said, "I don't understand. If you're having company, why do you need me?"

This time it was Matt who spoke. "Robert Osborn isn't company, he's the family attorney. He's coming tonight to settle Rory's estate."

Rory's estate! Good heavens, she'd never even thought about Rory having an estate! He was only twenty-two years old and a college student. What kind of estate could he have? She wondered if she was in for even more problems.

Robert Osborn arrived a few minutes later, and he proved to be a rather unimpressive man of about Jim's age. He carried a large leather briefcase and emptied the contents on the desk while Matt poured drinks. He handed Anne a glass of amber liquid that had been poured over ice cubes. She'd never tasted liquor before, except for a glass of wine— once. She toyed with the glass for a few minutes while the others visited, and then she finally took a large gulp. It was like liquid fire pouring down her throat!

She put the glass down quickly and gasped with an intake of breath that ended in a spell of choking. Matt was beside her immediately, pulling her out of her chair and onto her feet as he pounded her on the back. She coughed and sputtered and tears streamed down her cheeks. Her lungs felt as if they would burst if they didn't get some air. Matt held her, patted her back and soothed her until finally the choking stopped and she was able to take a deep breath.

"What on earth did you give her?" Jim demanded angrily.

119

"Scotch on the rocks," Matt muttered as he held her cheek against his chest.

Jim was furious. "Why did you do a stupid thing like that? You should have known she'd choke!"

Matt shook his head. "She told me Scotch on the rocks was her favorite drink."

Anne lifted her head to look at him, denial written all over her face. "When did I tell you that?"

His eyes held hers. "Several months ago—on the phone." He frowned, "You don't drink at all, do you?"

She shook her head; there was no point in denying it. She'd managed to mess things up again. Matt's arms tightened as he held her to him, but his words were whispered for her alone. "What kind of game are you playing, little girl?"

She could feel the erratic beat of his heart under her cheek, but then he led her back to her chair and seated himself across the room from her. She felt as if part of her had been torn away.

Robert Osborn got their attention and began to speak. "As I assume you all know, Rory died intestate; that is, without making a will. He made the mistake so many of us make, that of believing himself too young to die."

Anne shifted in her seat. Too young to die? Oh, yes, Rory was that, and so was Angela. And if there *was* a baby . . . She made herself listen to what the attorney was saying. "Most of Rory's estate was tied up in trusts which are under the control of trustees—"

Again Anne's mind wandered. All those whereases and whyfores made little sense to her. This talk of estates and trusts was like a foreign language, and, besides, it had nothing to do with her. She wished she could go to her room, get away from Matt sitting there so calmly, listening to every word. Matt had a brilliant mind. He could understand everything, everything but how much she loved him. And he was too deeply prejudiced against Angela to ever fall in love with Anne. Oh, she appealed to him physically, he desired her, but it could never be anything deeper than that. He'd never let himself fall in love with his brother's wife. Widow, she reminded herself. Besides, he had Polly Parker.

Anne knew she could never love anyone but Matt—and Jim. Her love for Jim was vastly different from the passion she felt for Matt, but no less deep. Jim was the father she'd longed for all her life.

This morning she'd made up her mind to leave, to get out of here while she still had her sanity, but Matt had shown her how impossible that was. Jim's very life depended on her presence here and the loving care she could give him. She was trapped in this magnificent house with one man who both hated and desired her and another who literally couldn't live without her.

It was more than she could bear to think about, and she forced her attention back to the present just as she became aware that someone was talking to her. "Angela, are you listening?"

It was Robert Osborn, and Anne had been caught woolgathering. She flushed and stammered, "I—I'm sorry, were you speaking to me?"

He frowned. "I'm afraid I have been for quite some time. I've been telling you that you can't touch the principal of your husband's estate but that you will receive interest checks every month that should be sufficient for you to live comfortably."

Interest checks? For her? What on earth was the man talking about? She cleared her throat and said, "I'm afraid I don't understand. Who is going to send me interest checks?"

She felt the eyes of all four of them gazing at her with astonishment. Constance gave a little shudder of disgust as Mr. Osborn found his voice. "Angela, as Rory's widow you are entitled to a sizable part of his estate. I've just told you that it's tied up in trusts but that you will receive the interest. It should come to, oh, roughly—" He named a figure that left Anne gasping. It was practically what most of the people she knew made in a year and it would be coming in every *month!*

Anne sank back, too shocked to respond. The others continued to watch her, waiting for her to say something. When she didn't, Matt spoke. He sounded sarcastic. "What's the matter, isn't it enough for you? Did Rory neglect to tell you he had very little money of his own? Still, that must be considerably more than you made every month as a waitress."

She heard Jim speak sharply to Matt but didn't bother to sort out the words. Was there no end to the repercussions of her deception? It had started out so simply. She would just play along with everybody, let Matt think she was Angela, Rory's wife. Go home with Matt and let the Hawthornes take care of her until she was in a position to take care of herself. What harm could it do?

She sighed inwardly. If she'd had any idea of the

harm she could do, she would have taken her chances with Aunt Martha and Clarence. The masquerade had grown into a nightmare that was making her life a horror of frustrations and recriminations. She was hopelessly ensnared. There was money involved, lots of it. If she admitted she wasn't Rory's wife, they could charge her with attempting to defraud his estate. Now she knew she could be arrested!

Anne slowly pushed herself up from the chair and stood. She didn't look at anyone but kept her eyes focused on a spot just above Robert's head as she spoke, hardly above a whisper. "Excuse me, I'm suddenly very tired and I don't feel well."

She hurried upstairs to her room and collapsed on the bed.

Anne slept late the next morning and when she woke, she had no desire to get out of bed. Her muscles ached from the long walk yesterday and she had things to sort out in her mind. Rory's widow had inherited a large amount of money, but Anne wasn't Rory's widow. If she accepted those monthly checks it would be stealing, and if she didn't, how could she possibly explain it to everyone concerned?

It occurred to her that if she handled things right she could be rich. She could have her own apartment. Her own sports car. She could travel, do anything she wanted.

She could also go to prison!

Anne shivered and realized that even without the shadow of prison she wouldn't want the money. She was rich now, or at least she lived as if she were, and it had brought her nothing but pain and unhappiness. She had to get away from Matt before he broke her into a million tiny pieces—but she couldn't leave Jim.

She wondered how long it would be before Jim's health improved. Wolf had said he would be able to use his arm and leg if he would do his exercises. Maybe under Wolf's supervision she could work with him, encourage him to help himself. It was his blood pressure everyone worried about. Surely if he was more independent, able to move around, he would no longer be so depressed and frustrated and his blood pressure would settle down.

At lunch time Anne found Jim waiting for her in the small, sunny breakfast room. He greeted her and indicated the seat next to him. She kissed him lightly and sat down as she said, "I'm glad we're having lunch in here, but where are the others?"

Jim rang for the maid to start serving and answered, "Constance has a hospital board meeting and Matt is gone."

"Gone?" Anne was watching the maid serve the spicy French onion soup and only half listening. "Where did he go?"

Jim frowned. "Didn't he tell you? He left early this morning for Utah."

Anne's spoon clattered against her soup bowl. "Utah! Why on earth did he go to Utah?"

"You mean you didn't know? Didn't he say goodbye?"

Anne shook her head, her appetite suddenly gone. "No, I had no idea he was leaving. When will he be back?"

"I don't know." Jim watched her carefully. "He shouldn't be gone more than a week."

A cold chill shook her. Matt was gone. But why should it hurt so? Wasn't this what she'd wanted, to put as much distance as possible between herself and Matt? So why did she feel so desolate, so deserted?

Jim looked away from her and continued talking. "Apparently no one has explained our business setup to you. I'm chairman of the board and Matt is president of one of the nation's leading uranium exploration and development mining companies. Matt is a geologist and often goes on our exploratory projects. The one in Utah is having some problems and Matt felt he could handle them best by being on the site. He left early this morning."

Anne nodded, numb with misery. "I see."

Jim put his big hand over her fist. "Anne, have you and Matt been quarreling?"

Anne couldn't think straight enough to lie. "Yes."

"What about?"

"Matt doesn't like me very much."

Jim looked puzzled. "That's not the impression I got. Why doesn't he like you?"

She couldn't tell him the whole truth, but neither could she evade his question. "He doesn't think I was a good wife to Rory." She looked at Jim and her eyes were bright with unshed tears. "None of you do. The whole family was upset when Rory married." She was careful not to say, "married *me.*"

Jim sighed and brought her hand to his freshly shaven cheek. "I won't deny that we were upset at first. None of us knew you then, but that's no longer true. Surely you know how I feel about you? You couldn't be dearer to me if you were my own daughter."

Anne's fingers caressed his cheek. "Matt doesn't want you to love me."

Jim smiled. "Matt's jealous."

Her eyes widened with surprise. "Oh, no. He's afraid I'll hurt you."

"Will you?" Jim's voice was soft.

Anne shook her head. "No, never. I'd die first. You're the only father I've ever known and I love you."

Before Jim could answer the maid came back with a steaming casserole of something that smelled of shrimp and mushrooms, and Anne quickly put her hand in her lap. They ate in silence for awhile, then Jim said, "I almost forgot. Robert left some papers for you to sign before he can turn Rory's interest checks over to you."

Anne's breath caught in her throat. Her decision regarding the inheritance would have to come sooner than she'd expected. Well, why not? There was only one thing she could do, and she might as well get it over with. She bit her lip and said, "Jim, I don't want to sign any papers. I don't want that money."

Jim stared at her, astonished. "But the money's yours! You'll need it to live on."

She looked down at her plate. "I'll get a job."

"A job!" He was almost shouting. "You mean go back to work as a waitress?"

"No!" Anne hadn't the faintest idea how to wait on tables and she'd momentarily forgotten that

126

Angela had been a waitress. A sudden thought occurred to her. "I can't work as a waitress with my arm in a cast. I thought maybe I could work as a salesperson while I go to school."

Jim shook his head in disbelief. "School? You mean you want to go back to Radcliffe? Your tuition's paid through the rest of the year, but I'd hoped you'd stay here, at least for awhile." He sounded disappointed.

"Oh, no, I don't want to go back to Radcliffe!" Anne felt as if she was in quicksand, sinking deeper with every word. "I thought maybe I could enroll in a secretarial school here in Denver. I—I have a little money and maybe I could borrow what I don't have. Take out a student loan."

"Anne! You don't have to borrow money; I'll give you any amount you want!" Jim's voice was tight with indignation. "Have Matt and Constance really made you feel so unwelcome that you think you have to go to work? By heavens, I'll—"

He banged his fist on the table and Anne forgot her own problems in her concern for him. He was much too upset! She took his hand in hers and outshouted him. "Jim, no! It's not like that. Please, calm down." She twisted her hands together in agitation. "Matt was right, I do hurt you, even when I don't mean to. Your blood pressure—"

He made an effort to calm himself. "It's all right. A little healthy temper tantrum isn't going to hurt me." His hand tightened on hers. "Now tell me why you think you have to go to school and learn to be somebody's errand girl when I need you right here at home?"

Anne attempted a smile. "If I thought that was true I'd be happy to stay here with you, but you have Wolf, and the servants—and Mrs. Hawthorne, of course."

Jim lifted Anne's chin and forced her to look at him. "Constance *has* been nasty to you, hasn't she?"

"No," Anne said, "not really. She ignores me mostly."

He kissed her forehead. "I'm aware that that is a very potent form of abuse, but Rory was Constance's baby. He came along many years after we thought there would be no more children, and she was always possessive of him. She would have been difficult with any girl Rory married. Constance is not one to show her emotions, but Rory's death was a great blow to her. Please try not to be hurt by her attitude." Then he quickly changed the subject. "But we've wandered far afield from the original problem, which was whether or not you would go to work. I have a compromise solution. If I enroll you in the best business school in Denver, will you agree not to work until you've graduated?"

Anne nodded, surprised by his offer. "Of course, if that's what you want. I'll pay you back, I promise."

Jim's eyes narrowed and his voice hardened "Don't start that again! If it means so much to you to be independent, I'll make you my personal assistant and you'll earn every cent I spend on you."

A thought occurred to Anne and she shook her head. "No, Jim, I'm going to work directly under Wolf. I'll get him to teach me what exercises you should be doing and I'll see that you do them. I'm warning you, I can crack the whip pretty hard and I intend to have you walking again very soon."

A look of relief softened Jim's face and he grinned. "You little trickster, that's what you had in mind all the time, isn't it? Shame on you for taking advantage of a sick old man! As soon as I'm back on my feet I'm going to chase you down and paddle you where it will do the most good!"

They both dissolved in gales of laughter.

Chapter Seven

Jim enrolled Anne in a private business school, but since the new term didn't start until after Christmas, he arranged for his secretary, Lester Burns, to start instructing her in filing, bookkeeping and general office procedures. Anne and Lester worked together during the afternoons in Jim's office at the house.

Anne spoke to Wolf about starting regular physical therapy sessions for Jim. Since Jim had done the exercises before Rory's death and was fairly proficient, they advanced rapidly. By the end of the first week he had graduated to walking therapy.

Then Matt came home! He appeared as quickly as he had disappeared—at breakfast. He'd been gone six days when Anne came downstairs one morning and found him sitting at the table in the breakfast room with a cup of coffee and the newspaper, just as if he had never been gone.

Her relief was so great that she leaned against the

door frame, afraid her rubbery knees wouldn't hold her. He looked up, and for a moment their eyes held and an electric current vibrated between them. Anne was the first to look away. She knew if she didn't she'd run to him, throw her arms around him, make a fool of herself.

When Matt spoke it was as if he had seen her only minutes before. "Good morning, Anne. Come in and have some breakfast."

Just like that. No "How have you been," or "I missed you." Just a casual greeting.

Anne stood there, unwilling to leave the support of the door behind. She took a deep breath and hoped her voice wouldn't tremble as she said, "Hello, Matt. Did you have a nice trip?"

He nodded and motioned her to the chair across from him. "We managed to straighten out the problem; I guess you could say it was successful." She walked to the table and sat down as he continued. "Dad says you've been making him do his exercises."

"You've seen Jim?" Anne asked, surprised.

"Not yet. I didn't get in until late last night, but I spoke to him on the phone several times. I have to admire you, Anne, you really know how to get to him. He thinks you're a combination of Florence Nightingale and a Botticelli nymph."

Anne slumped. So that's how it was going to be. Why couldn't she understand that he was always going to be suspicious of her motives? She brushed a lock of hair off her cheek. "I gather you don't approve."

His eyebrow raised in a sardonic salute. "How can

131

I object to anything that will help Dad get back the use of his arm and leg? I assume you *are* getting results?"

She was getting tired of Matt's sarcasm and pushed back her chair as she rose. "You're welcome to come and see for yourself. We have sessions every morning from ten until eleven." She walked out of the room and had breakfast in the kitchen with Wolf.

Matt was waiting with Jim and Wolf when Anne entered the exercise room at exactly ten o'clock. She ignored Matt and got Jim positioned for his range-of-motion exercises. She put him through them while Wolf supervised and Matt watched.

Matt came again the next morning and for several mornings thereafter to help where he could or just watch as Anne gently bullied Jim into letting Wolf put him through the painful exercises. The skeptical looks with which he'd favored her the first morning gave way to a certain grudging respect.

Then came the day that Jim made his first solo trip across the room in the walker. Matt gave Anne a look of genuine admiration and a smile and stopped coming, apparently satisfied that she was sincere in her effort to help his father.

Anne answered the door one afternoon to admit a well-dressed young man who said he had an appointment with Jim. That evening Jim called Anne into the den. He motioned her to sit beside him on the couch facing the warm, soothing fire and got right to the point. "Anne, I've been thinking about your refusal to accept your share of Rory's estate. I want you to have it, and maybe later we can work something out, but for now would it be satisfactory with you if we leave the trust funds as they are? I'll reinvest the interest and pay you a salary for the services you're performing for me here. You'll be in school for a year and after that we can talk about this again."

Anne breathed a sigh of relief. Jim was being amazingly cooperative. She'd been afraid he'd put up a fuss and insist on knowing why she didn't want the money, but instead he was accepting her refusal with a counterproposal that she could accept. Apparently the young man who had visited Jim that afternoon was an investment counselor.

It puzzled her, but she was too relieved to worry about it. She had just one request. "Please don't tell Matt I've refused the inheritance." Matt would think it was still another way Anne had devised to win Jim's approval. Again Jim agreed without argument.

The Christmas season was approaching, but Constance refused to acknowledge it with cards, decorations or parties. When Jim mentioned it she said, "I couldn't face the frivolity of Christmas with Rory gone." A flash of pain crossed her face as she swallowed and hurried on. "It's too soon, James. No one expects it of us. We'll attend the midnight Christmas Eve service as usual, but I'm refusing all other invitations." Jim reached over and took her hand and Anne excused herself and left the room quietly.

Matt surprised Anne one morning with the announcement that he had made an appointment for her to see Dr. George Koenig, the family physician Anne had met at Rory's funeral. She protested that

133

she felt fine, but Matt was adamant. She knew there was no use arguing and went to get dressed. Matt was waiting for her with the car when she came back downstairs.

He drove to Dr. Koenig's office by way of the Civic Center and pointed out to Anne the gold-domed state capitol building built entirely of Colorado granite, the city and counties building with its elongated U-shape and its Ionic and Corinthian columns. Matt said it was known as one of the most beautiful government buildings in the world, and Anne could believe it. The unique Denver Art Museum building was a work of art in itself, with its shimmering facade of over a million gray glass tiles and its unusual random window patterns, arranged to prevent direct sunlight from touching delicate art objects.

Matt seemed to enjoy Anne's appreciation of his city's famous buildings and insisted that no visit to Denver was complete without at least viewing the huge old United States Mint, which, he explained, had first opened its doors in September, 1863, as an assay office. By the time they got to the medical building the tension between them was gone and they were actually laughing.

Dr. Koenig saw nothing to laugh about as he poked and probed, and later, when he faced Anne and Matt in his office, he said, "I know you've had a lot on your mind, Angela, with your husband's tragic death, but you really shouldn't have neglected your own health so carelessly."

Anne shifted in her seat and wondered what he

was getting at. Matt frowned as the doctor continued, "It's been almost three weeks since you left the hospital in Nebraska. As far as I can tell you're recovering well enough but we can't be sure without tests and X-rays. And you *are* too thin and run down." He turned to Matt. "I want to put her in the hospital tomorrow for a couple of days. It will take that long to complete the workup I want done."

Matt's face was inscrutable as he said, "Of course, whatever you think best. Are there any problems?"

He might as well have been discussing his dog with the vet for all the emotion he showed, Anne thought bitterly.

Dr. Koenig shook his head. "I doubt it, but we want to make sure she's healing properly. She had multiple injuries, and, in my opinion, she never should have been dismissed from the hospital so soon. I'll call in Leonard Stahl; he's the best orthopedist in the area."

Anne protested. "But I feel fine. Couldn't you just do the tests and X-rays here in the office? Two days in the hospital will cost a fortune."

Dr. Koenig chuckled as he rose and came around the desk to help Anne to her feet. "I hardly think you need to worry about the expense, Angela. The insurance will cover most of it, but James has given instructions that you're to have the best available medical care." He took her arm and escorted her to the door. "You're a very special young lady, my dear, and neither James nor I intend to let anything happen to you."

Matt snorted as he led her into the hall. "So poor

old Koenig's smitten with you too. Isn't Dad enough? Do you have to collect men like other women collect coupons?"

Anne gasped and opened her mouth to retort, but he gave her no chance as he opened the heavy glass door and shoved her out into the parking lot. His voice was harsh as he said, "I'd advise you to concentrate on George Koenig; he's a widower, so at least you won't be breaking up a marriage."

She pulled away from him, stung by his biting charges, a quick fury building inside her. "You filthy-minded beast!" She turned to face him, her hair ruffled by the wind. "I'm sick of your accusations, but I'm not surprised. You wouldn't recognize a tender emotion if it hit you. It's no wonder you can't distinguish between the various types of love. You've never felt *any* of them!"

Before she could see them coming, Matt's hands were on her shoulders, roughly pulling her to him. His expression was grim as he grated, "You think not?" and crushed her against him as his mouth ground into hers, forcing her lips apart, deliberately cruel.

She kicked and pounded at him with her left hand but she was no match for his strength. His arms were squeezing the breath from her and the pressure of his mouth on hers was painful. With one last desperate effort she twisted her head away from him and broke free. She put her hand to her bruised mouth and her voice shook with rage. "That's not love! That's raw, unbridled lust—and how like you it is not to know the difference!"

TO START AGAIN

They drove home in silence and she didn't see him again until the next morning. She had no idea where he went for dinner, and she tried futilely to convince herself that she didn't care.

When Anne woke, it was snowing and apparently had been for some time. A strong wind blew it into white drifts against buildings, fences and trees, and she shivered in her thin nightgown, even though the controlled heating system kept the house warm no matter what the temperature was outside. It was still very early, but she knew she would have to dress soon. They were expecting her at the hospital within the hour.

Yesterday Jim had insisted that he would take her to the hospital in the chauffeur-driven limousine, but that was before this storm had battered its way across the mountain peaks and into Denver. She'd have to make him understand that he couldn't go out in this weather. She could take a cab.

She answered a knock on the door absently, assuming it was Bess. Instead, Matt strode in, impatient as usual. It seemed to her that he looked tired, as though he hadn't slept well. *It figures,* she thought with a jab of pain. *He probably spent the night with Polly.*

His gaze ranged over her scantily clad form as he said, "You'd better get dressed so we can leave; it will be slow-going in this storm."

She glared at him. "We?"

He nodded briskly. "You didn't really think I'd let Dad go out in this weather, did you?"

137

So she was in the wrong again. It never occurred to him that she might be as concerned over Jim's health as he was.

She was uneasy in her low-cut, lightweight nightgown, but Matt had seen her in less and she knew he would mock her, if only with his eyes, if she reached for her robe. Instead, she said, "There's no need for you to go out in the storm either; I'll call a cab."

His hands clenched into fists and she could see the anger building in him as he replied, "Grow up, Anne, and quit sulking like a spoiled child. You know that if I don't take you Dad will. Now get your clothes on and I'll wait for you downstairs."

They drove to the hospital in the strained silence that was so common between them, but once they arrived there was no waiting in drafty halls to be seen by an overworked intern as had been the case in the public clinics where she had been treated in Chicago the few times she'd been sick. Here they were escorted immediately to a large, luxurious private room and welcomed by the hospital administrator. Anne was astounded.

Matt stayed until Dr. Koenig came with Dr. Stahl, the orthopedic surgeon. The two doctors talked to Matt for quite awhile. After he left, the testing began. For two days a steady stream of nurses and technicians took her temperature and her blood, gave her injections and pills and wheeled her back and forth to X-ray.

The storm continued unabated outside, but Jim talked to her on the phone morning and evening and sent several bouquets of flowers. Matt neither came nor called until the morning of the third day.

Sometime during the night the storm had blown itself out and the morning was bright and sunny. Dr. Koenig appeared early to examine her new, lighter weight cast and dismiss her. He told her she was healing rapidly and they should be able to remove the cast in another three weeks, but that she had to make an effort to eat better and sleep more.

Anne had just finished dressing when Matt appeared. He glanced around the room at the masses of floral arrangements and muttered, "It's a good thing you're coming home. Now maybe Dad can think of something besides talking to you on the phone every few minutes and ordering flowers."

She was grateful for Jim's concern, but she wished Matt had missed her a little too.

As he guided the car through the snow-covered streets he seemed quiet and subdued but not angry. She peeked at him out of the corner of her eyes; there was a tenseness about him that was unsettling.

She sighed and leaned back and he glanced at her and said, "Are you tired?"

She shook her head. "No; I've been in bed for two days. I'd like to take a long walk."

He swerved to miss a snowdrift that stretched into the street. "Don't do that unless someone goes with you. We don't want to lose you again."

She looked at him. There was no trace of sarcasm in his voice. He changed the subject. "Did they tell you that your ribs are healed and the head injury shouldn't cause any more problems? Your arm is doing very well, too, and you won't have to wear the cast much longer."

She gasped. "How do you know all this?"

He shrugged. "I talked to George Koenig, of course."

So he wasn't as uncaring as she'd thought. She wondered if she'd ever understand him. It was a few minutes before he spoke again, and when he did it was with reluctance. "Anne, I'm leaving for Australia in the morning."

His words cut through her like the thrust of a knife. She leaned forward slightly, as though to protect herself, but it was no use; the pain refused to abate. She took a deep breath and said, "Oh?"

He nodded. "We have a new exploration project there. I'd intended to go over with the team when they left, but then Rory—" He paused. "I was needed here, but now everything's under control again, and, thanks to you, Dad is getting better every day. I can go now and know I won't be missed."

"I'll miss you, Matt." The words were out before she could stop them, and she bit her lip in dismay, wishing she could call them back.

The car swerved again and this time there was no snowdrift. Matt reached out and took her hand. "Will you, Anne?"

It was too late to retract her words; she might as well confess. She nodded and he squeezed her hand, continuing to hold it in his own as he said, "I'd like us to part friends. I'll be gone several weeks and I don't want to have to worry about you."

Anne's eyes opened in amazement. Why would he worry about her? He must have meant he didn't want to worry about his father and he wanted to be sure he could trust her to get in touch with him should anything go wrong.

He continued talking. "If you feel up to it, I'd like to take you to dinner tonight. You haven't seen Larimer Square yet; we can eat at one of the restaurants and then take in a performance at the theater."

Anne had never wanted anything so much as she wanted to spend the evening with Matt, but she never knew when he was going to turn on her, slash her with words and leave her wounded and unable to defend herself. She couldn't deliberately court that kind of treatment.

She licked her lips and murmured, "Do you think we can get along for a whole evening?"

Matt's hand tightened on hers. "I'll be a gentleman, I promise. I usually am; it's only when you torment me that I lose control."

Anne sat forward, blinking. "*I* torment *you!* It's *you* who torments *me!*"

He pulled the car over and stopped, then turned to look at her. "We torment each other, Anne." He leaned over and kissed her lips, then caressed them with his finger. "I'm sorry I hurt you Wednesday. I didn't mean to. I wanted—" A flicker of anguish clouded his eyes and was gone as he reached across her to open her door. "We'd better go in. Dad's anxiously waiting to see you."

Anne realized for the first time that they were parked in front of the house.

That evening they toured Larimer Square, a charming restoration of Larimer Street as it had been in the early days of Denver. Matt guided Anne through courtyards, promenades and quaint shops in handsomely restored buildings of Civil War vintage.

141

Anne was enchanted by the glow of gaslights in the darkened streets.

They took their time over their meal. First a mussel soup, then a saddle of lamb with a mousse of veal. Dessert was a pear on a crispy bit of deep-fried pastry with a chestnut sauce, and the wine was a French cabernet. Anne had never eaten such food before, and she savored every mouthful as Matt entertained her with a thumbnail sketch of the history of Denver.

His dark eyes were bright with interest and his hands moved expressively as he said, "Denver was established during the raucous, brawling Pike's Peak gold rush in the middle eighteen hundreds, when people came by the thousands in search of instant riches. Two small settlements along Cherry Creek were consolidated and named Denver after Governor James W. Denver of the Kansas Territory."

Matt watched with amusement as Anne licked chestnut sauce from her fingers, then continued. "For years the city's fortunes were dependent on the rise and fall of the gold camps. One year a fire reduced half the business district to ashes, and a few months later a flash flood inundated the area and killed twenty people.

"The coming of the railroads stabilized the economy a bit, but Denver didn't really begin to grow as a city until the great silver discoveries at Leadville, Aspen and in the San Juan Mountains around 1880." He signaled the waiter for the check and smiled at Anne. "Now Denver is one of the great trade and transportation centers of the nation, and I think I've bored you long enough with my history lesson." He pushed back his chair and stood. "Come on. If we don't leave now, we'll be late for the theater."

Much later, they stopped at the ultramodern Denver Hilton for a drink. They found a tiny half-moon-shaped booth in a corner, just big enough for two in the dimly lit room, and Matt remembered to order a plain cola for Anne. Soft music drifted in from the next room, where there was dancing, and Matt covered Anne's hand with his as he smiled down at her. "Have you had a nice time so far?"

Anne was sure her face was glowing with happiness as she raised it to him and said simply, "It's been the most wonderful evening of my whole life."

Matt frowned. "It's not necessary to lie, Anne."

She caught her breath at the abruptness of his words, and her first instinct was denial. "But I'm not lying—" Then she remembered. Angela, as Rory's wife, would have had hundreds of wonderful evenings at parties, theaters, dances. Somehow, she had to make Matt understand. She touched his face with the fingers of her left hand and murmured, "Please believe me. I've never enjoyed a night out so much before."

His eyes bored into her as if trying to see into her mind, then his lips touched hers and his arms went around her, drawing her close as the kiss deepened but remained gentle. Her whole being responded to his tenderness as he cradled her to him and buried his face in her silky, golden hair. Her heart fluttered wildly and she could feel the erratic beat of his pulse where her lips caressed his throat.

After a moment, he said softly, "Will you really miss me while I'm gone?"

She knew she should be on her guard, that she shouldn't trust Matt, but when he held her so close, kissed her with such gentle hunger, she melted into a throbbing mass of emotions that knew neither caution nor restraint. She whispered against his ear. "Oh, yes."

That seemed to please him and he relaxed a little and took a sip of his drink. They sat quietly, listening to the music, his arm around her, her head on his shoulder. Anne asked a question that had been plaguing her. "Matt, when you went to Utah, why didn't you tell me you were leaving?"

His answer was frank and without hesitation. "I had to get away from you before you drove me clear out of my mind, and I was afraid if I tried to say goodbye I'd never leave."

She sighed and looked up at him. "I'm sorry you don't like me."

With a soft groan his mouth covered hers in a hard, swift kiss and then he stood, pulling her out of the booth with him as he said, "Stop talking nonsense and let's dance."

The ballroom was large but intimately lighted, the music was slow and sensual and the dance floor was crowded. Matt put both arms around her waist. Her right arm was immobilized in the cast, but she put her left one around his neck and snuggled against him as they began to sway to the rhythm of the orchestra.

The low, throbbing beat of the waltz surrounded them, fusing them together in an intimacy that left Anne quivering with feelings she hadn't known she was capable of. Matt's lips brushed her cheek and his arms tightened as though he couldn't get close enough to her. She followed his steps expertly as they wove slowly through the other couples without really being aware of them, or of anything but each other. Neither of them spoke, afraid of breaking the enchanted spell.

Then the music stopped and the lights brightened. Matt gave Anne a quick hug and, without taking his arm from around her waist, started leading her off the floor. At first Anne didn't see the other couple, but she recognized the familiar throaty, sensuous voice. "Matt, darling!"

It was Polly, looking stunning as always, on the arm of a tall, good-looking man. Her contemptuous glance raked over Anne before she turned her attention back to Matt. Her voice was smooth and suggestive as she said, "So this is the 'duty' you had to perform tonight. How sweet of you to take poor little Anne out on your last night at home." She smiled at Anne, but her eyes were cold and calculating. She continued to speak to Matt. "I'm all packed and ready to go, darling. Be sure to pick me up early; we don't want to miss the plane. I just can't wait to get you all to myself in Australia."

Anne was paralyzed by Polly's words. She couldn't even cry out when the pain exploded deep inside her and spread. So her evening with Matt had been a *duty* he felt he must perform for his poor unattractive sister-in-law who couldn't attract an escort of her own! He was taking Polly to Australia with him! Combining business and pleasure. A lovers' vacation away from the prying eyes of family and friends. And in spite of that he was making an all-out effort to seduce Anne!

She heard him saying her name, but she turned and, with as much dignity as she could muster, walked across the room to the women's lounge, where she sat down heavily on the couch. She felt dizzy and she got up, only to sway unsteadily on her feet.

She splashed cold water on her white face as the restroom attendant stood by, wringing her hands and asking Anne if she felt faint. She'd really walked into it with her eyes open this time. She knew how much Matt disliked her, she had no reason to trust him, and still she'd jumped at the chance to let him hurt her again. And all because, fool that she was, she'd fallen in love with him.

There was no possibility of sneaking out without Matt seeing her. He was probably standing outside the door waiting. No, it was time she stood up and fought, for her self-respect if nothing else. She was through being a doormat for him to wipe his feet on.

She repaired her makeup and stood for a moment, wondering if she could really stand the pain of meeting Matt face to face. She'd never been so deeply humiliated, but she wasn't going to let either Matt or Polly know that.

She went to the row of telephones and called a cab, then braced herself and swept out the door and down the hall toward the entrance. She heard Matt call to her but she ignored him and kept on walking. He caught up with her at the checkroom and gave the girl behind the counter the stub as he said, "Anne, I'm sorry. I want to talk to you."

The girl came with their coats and Matt helped her into Angela's mink. She moved sharply away from his lingering hands and by some miracle kept her voice calm and cool. "But I don't want to talk to you, Matt. There's no reason for you to leave, I've called a cab. I'm sorry you felt obliged to entertain me tonight, but there's no longer any need. You're free to go back to Polly."

Matt glowered at her. "The devil I am! You're not leaving here without me, and you're going to listen to me if I have to tie you to a chair!"

His hands clamped around her shoulders, and, with a strength that surprised her, she twisted away and faced him, her voice tight with rage. "If you so much as lay a finger on me, I'll scream. I'll tell the security guards you're trying to make me leave with you against my will, and by tomorrow morning you and your precious family will be in the headlines of every newspaper in the area. I'm tired of this little game we've been playing, Matt. I'll concede I'm no match for you, but, as you pointed out the other day, George Koenig will be a pushover. He likes me and he has enough money to satisfy my expensive tastes. That's all I really care about, so go back to your raven-haired witch with the forked tongue and leave me alone."

She turned away and thanked the doorman as he opened the door and helped her into the waiting cab.

Chapter Eight

Anne attended the Christmas Eve candlelight service at church with Constance and Jim. It had been almost a week since Matt and Polly had left for Australia, and in the quiet of the poinsettia-decorated sanctuary Anne prayed to be released from the torment of the unrequited love she still felt for Matt in spite of the way he'd treated her. She didn't expect her prayer to be answered.

She hadn't seen Matt after she'd stormed out of the Denver Hilton, and, although Jim and Constance had talked to him the day after he arrived in Australia, he hadn't asked to talk to her. She wouldn't have spoken to him if he had. All she wanted was for him to stay away for as long as possible and leave her alone.

On Christmas morning the Hawthornes exchanged gifts with each other and the servants. Anne gave Constance the new novel everyone was

148

talking about and Jim a bottle of his favorite shaving lotion. Constance gave her a dress, black but very stylish, with sleeves wide enough to accommodate her cast.

She saved her gift from Jim until last. It was a small box containing a sterling silver identification tag and key ring with her name and the Hawthorne's address and phone number engraved on it. She grinned at Jim's subtle way of making sure she never got lost again. Then she noticed the attached key and exclaimed, "Hey, it even has a key to the house."

Jim stood, supporting himself with his walker, and reached down to pull her up off the floor where she was sitting by the fire. "That's not a house key. Come with me; I'll show you what it's for."

Anne followed along beside him as he made his slow, awkward way to the door with the support of the walker. Outside, on the porch, he pointed toward the driveway and said, "There, the key fits that."

Anne looked to where he was pointing and froze. There, standing majestically in the softly falling snow, was a gleaming midnight blue sports car, wrapped around with a wide red ribbon tied in a monsterous bow on the side facing them.

For a moment she felt a heady rush of excitement. Imagine her, Anne Greenfield, actually driving that magnificent piece of machinery! She could go anywhere she wanted, do anything she liked in a car like that. People would look at her and know she was rich, pampered and loved.

The excitement died. She wasn't rich, and the only reason Jim loved and pampered her was because he thought she was somebody else. The car was for Angela, not for Anne.

She turned to Jim and saw that Constance had joined them. Jim laughed and said, "It's for you, honey. Merry Christmas!"

The car sparkled in its newness and for a second Anne closed her eyes, hoping it was just an illusion that would be gone when she opened them. It wasn't. The car was still there, beckoning to her.

She swallowed and forced words through her numb throat. "Jim, Mrs. Hawthorne, I can't. I can't possibly accept such an expensive present. I—I'm overwhelmed!"

Jim interrupted. "Of course you can accept it. Put on your coat and I'll have Wolf take you for a ride and show you how to drive it."

Wolf handled the small car expertly and it seemed to purr under his experienced touch. Anne snuggled into the cream-colored leather seat and watched the scenery whiz past as they sped along the highway heading north toward Wyoming.

There was little traffic on this Christmas morning and on the return trip Wolf let Anne drive. She had no trouble controlling the car with one hand and was grateful for the automatic transmission. She wished she'd never let Jim talk her into taking it out, though; it would make it just that much harder to tell him she must refuse it.

When they got back to the house there were more packages. Special delivery gifts for Constance, Anne and Jim from Matt. Each received a jeweler's box containing opals cut with a gently rounded convex surface and reflecting brilliant flashes of color.

Jim's was mounted in a gold ring and Constance's in a pin surrounded by diamonds and emeralds. Anne caught her breath as she lifted hers from its red velvet-lined box. It was the most prized opal of all, a deep glowing black stone that flashed reds and yellows in addition to greens and blues. Circled by rubies and suspended from a gold chain, it was a pendant of black fire!

Anne stared, hypnotized by its glowing brilliance, as she held it up for Jim and Constance to see. They commented on its beauty and rarity and Jim explained that opals are mined extensively in Australia. Anne's attention was focused on the magnificent jewel. It must have cost a fortune, but why would Matt spend so much money on her now when he was always fussing about how much Angela had cost him in the past with her extravagant buying habits?

She slowly lowered the pendant back into its case and closed the lid. She'd send it back, of course. She couldn't possibly keep it. Angela would have accepted both the car and the jewel with eager delight, but if Anne was acting out of character, it was unavoidable. She couldn't accept such expensive gifts from Matt or Jim.

The next morning there was a letter in the mail for Anne from Matt. She burned it unopened in the fireplace, then took the opal pendant to the den where Jim was going over some papers and laid the case on the desk top as she said, "Will you please ask Lester to have this wrapped properly and returned to Matt? It will need to be insured, too. I'd do it myself but I'm not sure how to go about it."

Jim picked up the case and opened it. The jewel

flashed its brilliant colors in an almost pulsating manner. He looked up at her and said, "Why do you want to return this? It was a Christmas present. Matt will be hurt."

Anne shook her head. "It won't matter to him and it's much too expensive for me to accept."

Jim closed the case. "I assure you, Anne, Matt can well afford it."

Anne bit her lip. "Maybe he can but I can't. There's no way I could give him something of equal value. I—I don't want to be indebted to him any more than I already am."

"There's no reason for you to be indebted to anyone. You have more than enough money to buy gifts or whatever you want. It's just waiting for you to claim it. Rory's estate is yours Anne. Believe me, it's legally yours." Jim seemed intent on making her believe him.

Anne walked to the glass doors and looked out at the sun shining on the patio. The snow had stopped during the night and the sky was clear. "No, Jim." she said, "I told you, I don't want money from Rory. Just because you're stuck with me now doesn't mean you always will be. As soon as I've finished school I'll get a job and move to an apartment—"

His fist banged on the desk as he shouted, "Stop it! I won't hear any more of that kind of talk!"

He indicated the padded armchair on the other side of the desk and she sank into it. He sighed and said, "What happened the night before Matt left, Anne? You only pretend to eat and you walk around like a lost soul. When Matt calls he never asks about you but he manages to work the conversation around until I tell him you're fine. I get the feeling that if I told him you've lost weight and never laugh anymore, he'd catch the first plane home."

Anne jumped up, alarmed. "No, Jim, don't ever say that to Matt! Don't discuss me with him at all!"

Jim grunted. "Then you have been quarreling again. What happened, Anne? Why are you tormenting each other?"

She leaned back in the chair in an attitude of defeat. "You just don't understand. Matt doesn't like me. He only sent me a gift because it would have been rude not to. Now, please, will you send the pendant back for me?"

Jim seemed to shrink a little and he looked tired. "Yes, I'll send it. I'm not going to interfere at this point. Now, if there's nothing else, I *am* rather busy."

Anne stood. "I know; just one more thing and then I'll leave you alone. It's—it's about the car. Jim, I can't—"

He silenced her with a wave of his hand. "I don't want to hear it. I don't care what you do with the car. You can drive it, sell it or give it away. It's yours and I'm not going to take it back. Now, will you get out of here and let me work?"

Anne went upstairs to her room and threw herself across the bed. It wasn't yet noon and already she was tired. She knew there wasn't anything physically wrong with her; it was the beating her nerves were taking that left her exhausted. Why didn't Matt leave her alone? He'd humiliated her, degraded her beyond forgiveness, then sent her that lovely jewel, the gift of a lover. But he wasn't her lover. He was cavorting around Australia with Polly, and still he'd taken the time to select a very personal and expensive present. It didn't make sense.

Her thoughts turned to Jim. Jim was kind and thoughtful and she loved him, but now she'd made him mad at her too. She knew she'd hurt him by refusing the car but it wasn't meant for her. It was for Angela, and she wished she'd never heard of Angela Hawthorne. Why hadn't she told them in the beginning that she was just plain Anne Greenfield? That Angela Hawthorne was the dead girl?

Shortly before noon, Anne once again interrupted Jim in his den. He looked at her wearily and she knew he had been sitting at the desk for too long. She walked over to him and held out her hands. "Come on, let me help you over to the couch so you can stretch out for a few minutes before lunch."

He ran his hand over his face. "I am tired. I wonder if I'll ever be strong again."

He struggled to his feet and leaned on her as she helped him walk to the couch and lie down. She pushed a lock of white hair off his forehead and into place as she said, "Jim, I'm sorry I upset you about the car. I love it, and if you want me to have it, then I thank you very much for being so good to me." He smiled and relaxed as she continued. "There's just one thing I'd like to ask of you. Please don't register it in my name." He looked at her questioningly. "I'll feel better if it's your car. I'll keep it and drive it, but I'd rather not be the owner."

School started for Anne the first Monday of the new year, and it was a relief to have something to keep her busy. She liked her subjects and her teachers and learning came easily to her.

At the same time, Polly reappeared on the television news. Apparently her vacation time had run out.

A week later Dr. Stahl removed the cast from Anne's arm. It was like getting a new limb! She'd never appreciated the miracle of free movement until she'd had her arm bound in that cumbersome cast. Now it was gone, and while she was still somewhat limited in her arm movements, she once again had two hands. She could write, type and pull her own clothes on and off! It was sheer heaven.

Anne worked hard at school and at home, helping Jim overcome the damage to the muscles of his left side. On the days that were sunny and without the danger of snow or ice on the sidewalks, she took him for short walks in the fresh air. By the first of February he was able to walk with a three-legged cane and discard the hated walker. The healthy glow of color came back into his face and his blood pressure was no longer a problem.

During this time Anne received two more letters from Matt, both of which she also burned unopened. She didn't want to know what he was trying to say to her. If it was an excuse for his behavior, none would suffice; if it was more accusations against her, she wasn't going to read them. He'd gone too far this time and she'd never forgive him. She'd learn to live with the ever present pain that had plagued her since the scene at the Denver Hilton.

Matt had been gone six weeks when Wolf got the

call from his sister in North Dakota. Their elderly mother was having emergency surgery the following day and Wolf was advised to come at once. He hesitated about leaving Jim, but Anne assured him she could take over on the few occasions when Jim needed help.

The illness began very simply, with a cough. Anne heard it several times during breakfast before she realized Jim was coughing and not just clearing his throat.

She looked at him and frowned. "Do you feel all right? How long have you had that cough?"

Jim looked up from his newspaper. "I woke up with it, but it's nothing. Just a minor annoyance."

Anne had a busy schedule at school and left the house shortly afterwards without giving the matter another thought. That afternoon she put Jim through his exercises and everything seemed fine.

The next morning the cough was still with him and seemed deeper. Anne felt a twinge of concern and asked if he had any cough medicine.

Constance was annoyed with Anne's solicitude and interrupted. "I hardly think my husband's health is your problem, Angela. It's only a slight cold and he has the proper medication."

Anne took the hint and let the subject drop, but when she got home from school that afternoon he was still coughing and looked tired. She suggested they cancel the physical therapy session and he agreed.

Jim didn't appear for breakfast the following morning and Anne's concern grew. She questioned Constance, who answered abruptly, "James was disturbed several times during the night by spells of coughing, so he's sleeping in this morning." Anne started to speak, but Constance anticipated her question. "Apparently the medication he's taking is ineffective, so I called the pharmacy and asked them to send over something stronger."

When Anne got home from school she went immediately to Jim's second floor sitting room and cautiously pushed open the door. He was sitting by the fire, dressed in slacks and a heavy shirt, apparently dozing. Anne walked softly across the room and put her hand on his shoulder. There was a raspiness about his breathing that wasn't normal and she moved her hand to his cheek. It felt warm, but that could be due to his proximity to the fire.

He moved restlessly and opened his eyes as Anne said, "Are you sure you should be up, Jim? Wouldn't you rest more comfortably in bed?"

He took her hands and warmed them in his. "I'm glad you came, it's lonesome here all by myself. Sit down and talk to me."

She sat cross-legged on the floor beside him. "Where's Mrs. Hawthorne?"

He grunted. "She went shopping. She's flying to San Francisco tomorrow for an antique auction."

Anne was appalled. Did Constance really intend to go halfway across the country and leave her sick husband behind, alone and uncared for? Well, she amended, as she remembered all the servants, not really alone, but Wolf was no longer there to look after him. Anne was not convinced that his illness was just a simple cold.

Her reaction was stronger than she'd intended. "It

seems to me she should stay home and take care of you."

Jim chuckled and reached down to pat her on her blonde head. "You sound like a mama tiger protecting her cub, but I'm almost old enough to be your grandfather, little one, and I can take care of myself. Constance will only be gone a couple of days; I'll probably be over this cold by then."

Constance left before daylight the next morning in order to catch her early morning flight. Anne woke at her usual time and looked in on Jim. He was still asleep, but his breathing seemed somewhat labored and his face was pale and warm. She wondered if he was running a temperature but didn't want to wake him to take it. On the nightstand a half empty bottle of cough medicine and a sticky spoon were evidence that he'd been coughing during the night.

Anne left for school after instructing Bess to watch over Jim, but she couldn't keep her mind on her studies and finally gave up at noon and went home. She felt responsible for Jim now that Constance and Matt were gone. She knew very little about illness, though, only enough to know that Jim was getting worse instead of better.

He was still in bed but awake and propped up with pillows when she got there. His breathing was raspy and his temperature was 101 degrees.

She frowned and shook the thermometer down as she said, "This has gone on long enough; I'm going to call Dr. Koenig and ask him to stop over and take a look at you."

Jim waved a hand in dismissal. "George is attending a medical conference in New York."

Anne reached for the phone. "He must have another doctor covering for him. What's the number?"

"Put the phone down, Anne, and stop fussing. George's associate is a young idiot who doesn't know a thermometer from a stethoscope. I don't like him and I won't allow him to examine me."

A strong feeling of foreboding swept over her. If Jim were strong and healthy she wouldn't worry so much, but he wasn't. The stroke he'd suffered several months ago had taken a heavy toll, and she was afraid his once robust system might be too weakened to fight off another illness.

Why hadn't Constance insisted he see a doctor? It was her place to bully him into taking care of himself, not Anne's. Jim was fifty-five years old and a successful businessman. He wouldn't take orders from a twenty-year-old girl who'd had no experience with illness.

She gave him an aspirin and had his lunch sent up. Afterwards he slept but was disturbed at intervals by violent coughing spells. Again he refused to let her call a doctor. Anne was beside herself. If only Wolf were here! He was a nurse; he'd know what to do.

Anne kept giving Jim aspirin and liquids. That night she made herself a bed on the couch in his sitting room, but she didn't sleep much. Jim was restless and his breathing was labored.

By morning his temperature was 102 degrees and Anne was desperate. She had to have help, but she didn't know how to get in touch with Constance. Surely Jim must know where she was staying. She went to the desk in his sitting room and was going through his telephone index when the phone beside her rang. It was an overseas call from Australia. Matt! It was almost as if he had known how desperately she needed him.

His voice came through clear and strong and sent shivers down her back. "Anne? Is that you? Anne?"

"Matt! Oh, Matt, I'm so glad you called!" She choked on a sob as tears ran down her cheeks.

"Anne, what's the matter? Are you all right?" She knew he'd recognized her fear.

"It's Jim; he's sick. He's been sick for days and now his temperature is so high and he has trouble breathing—"

Her voice broke and for a minute she couldn't go on.

"What's the matter with Dad?" Matt demanded. "Where's Mother? What does the doctor say?"

"Your mother's in San Francisco and Dr. Koenig's in New York and Jim won't let me call his associate," she wailed. "Oh, Matt, I'm so scared. Mrs. Hawthorne says it's just a cold, but it's not. He keeps getting worse and I don't know what to do."

Matt swore. "Don't panic, Anne. Now listen carefully. Call Dr. Koenig's office and tell whatever doctor's on call just what you've told me, he'll take it from there. I know where Mother usually stays in San Francisco; I'll contact her and I'll be home just as soon as I can catch a flight."

Anne felt an immeasurable sense of relief. "Oh, Matt, please hurry, I need you."

Matt's voice on the other end was gentle. "Hang in there, honey, everything will be all right."

Things happened fast after Anne talked to the

doctor. Within the hour a physician who introduced himself as Dr. Chin, a chest specialist, arrived with an ambulance. When the attendants wheeled the stretcher into Jim's room to take him to the hospital, he refused to go.

The doctor reasoned and Anne pleaded but all he would say was, "When I die, it won't be in a hospital!"

Jim couldn't be admitted against his will so the doctor had no choice but to set up a mini-hospital in Jim's room. A nurse was summoned and he seemed more comfortable once he started getting oxygen.

It was late in the afternoon of the following day before Matt and Constance arrived. Anne had spent most of her waking hours at Jim's bedside, and she was fluffing up his pillows when the door opened and Constance walked in, followed by Matt. Anne's gaze flew to his face, hungry for the sight of him in spite of her determination not to be. His gaze on her was just as intense and the emotion that pulsated between them was shocking and powerful.

Anne pulled her attention back to Constance, who was speaking to her. "I—I'm sorry, what did you say?"

Constance was frowning. "I said, why isn't James in the hospital?"

"He—he wouldn't go." Anne stammered, feeling guilty, as though it were her fault.

Just then the nurse came in and Matt turned to talk to her as Constance hurried to Jim's bedside. Anne moved back to make room for her and then slipped quietly out the door into the sitting room, unwilling to intrude on their reunion.

She curled up in the chair in front of the fire and felt some of the tension drain from her. Matt was home. He'd take charge and make everything all right. Matt wouldn't let anything happen to Jim. Maybe now she could sleep for awhile.

She knew nothing more until she felt strong arms lifting her and carrying her down the hall. It was Matt; she'd know the feel of him anywhere. She put her arms around his neck and cradled her head in his shoulder as he carried her to her room and set her on her turned-down bed. She snuggled into the soft mattress as he removed her shoes and pulled the covers over her.

He sat on the edge of the bed and stroked her blonde curls as he said, "Dad says you've been caring for him continuously since he got sick." He leaned over and brushed his lips against hers, then changed the subject. "Did you read the letters I wrote you?"

She shook her head, too drowsy to open her eyes. She heard him murmur, "That's what I thought," and then he was gone.

The next two days were a nightmare. Jim was only partially conscious and his temperature was dangerously high. Matt and Constance took turns sitting by his bed. When Matt was there Anne sat with him, but when Constance came, Anne left the room. None of them slept for more than an hour at a time, and when Anne found Constance sobbing softly she was terrified. She'd never seen Jim's wife in tears, not even at the funeral of her youngest son. For his part, Matt barely spoke to Anne, and he didn't mention the letters again.

162

On the evening of the second day of the vigil Anne and Matt were sitting beside Jim's bed when Constance and Dr. Chin came in. Jim roused slightly and looked at them, then called Anne's name. She knelt by his bed and he put out his hand and stroked her tear-ravaged cheeks as he struggled to speak. "Don't cry, little daughter. I'll . . . take care . . . of you. Should . . . have . . . told you . . . sooner."

His hand dropped away and for a moment the only sound was the labored hoarseness of his breathing. Suddenly Constance's shrill, hysterical voice broke the silence. "Get her out of here! Get her out of my sight! It's not enough that she stole my son and came here to live against my wishes. Now she's bewitched my husband too. Get her out of my house!"

Anne knelt by the bed, petrified with shock, until Matt lifted her to her feet and led her out of the room and into the hall. "I'm sorry, Anne," he said. "Try to understand. Mother's under a fearful strain." He had his arm around her and was walking her down the hall. "She wants to be alone with Dad now, and you need to rest. You're exhausted." They'd reached the door to her room, and he opened it and stood aside. "I'll send Bess up to help you get ready for bed. Try to sleep."

Bess tucked Anne into bed and left, but Anne couldn't sleep. She tossed and turned, telling herself to stay away from Jim's room, she wasn't wanted there. Her restlessness increased.

The sense of urgency that had tugged at her all day became unbearable and she got out of bed, put on her champagne colored quilted robe and walked down the hall. She couldn't go into Jim's room, but neither could she stay away. She curled up on the window seat at the end of the hall with her legs drawn up and her face buried in her knees.

She was still there an hour later when Matt came out of Jim's room. He looked drawn and unbearably weary as he leaned back against the door and closed his eyes. Anne uttered a muffled gasp and he looked up and saw her. For a moment her heart stopped beating, then he smiled. She stared at him in disbelief as the smile grew and he said, "His temperature is down and he's breathing more normally. He's going to be all right, Anne. The worst is over and Dad's going to live."

The relief that surged through her was overwhelming and for a moment she didn't react at all. Then the tears came and with them great choking sobs that shook her whole body. Matt was beside her in an instant, his arms holding her, comforting her as he said, "Anne, he's all right, he's going to live. Don't cry like that, he's going to get well."

She couldn't answer, she could only nod her head as he held her close. After a long time her tears subsided and she lay against him, totally spent. He wiped her tear-stained face with his handkerchief, then picked her up and carried her to his room, where he deposited her between the sheets of his large bed.

She knew she shouldn't allow this. It was Polly Matt wanted, and Anne wasn't going to substitute for her in his bed or anywhere else, but when she tried to protest he barked, "Be quiet," and removed her robe. All the vitality had drained out of her and she could only lie there silently watching as he stripped to his briefs and slid in beside her.

He turned off the bedside lamp and reached for her in the dark as she made one last effort to resist. "Matt, don't. Please, I—"

He pulled her roughly to him and his voice was strained and harsh as he said, "Go to sleep, Anne; we're both exhausted. Tonight we need each other. Tomorrow, if you insist, we can argue about whether or not it was proper."

She snuggled against him and was asleep almost before he stopped talking.

Chapter Nine

Anne woke slowly to the feel of a feather brushing down the valley between her breasts. She shifted away from it but it followed her. She realized now that it wasn't a feather, it was too substantial for that. She moved again and opened her eyes to encounter a pair of brown velvet ones gazing down at her.

She wakened fully as Matt lowered his head and once more trailed light kisses down her partially exposed breast. Sensual pleasure tingled through her as she gasped, "Matt! What are you doing in my bed?"

He looked up and grinned. "You've got it backwards, Anne. It's *you* who's in *my* bed."

She fought against the sensuous languor that was stealing through her limbs and pushed his head, trying to dislodge his distracting lips. "Matt, stop that! I've got to see how Jim is."

166

She tried to roll away, but Matt's arm imprisoned her against him as he murmured, "Lie still; Dad's temperature is normal and he's sleeping peacefully. I just checked on him."

He nuzzled the side of her neck and his hands roamed slowly over her slender body, leaving tendrils of fire wherever they lingered. She knew she shouldn't let him do this, but she couldn't remember why. He'd been gone so long and she'd missed him so dreadfully. If she let him make love to her maybe he wouldn't need Polly.

Polly! He'd taken Polly to Australia with him! The memory shot through her like an electric charge and she wrenched herself away from Matt and tried to dive off the edge of the bed, but he was too quick for her. He caught her around the waist and hauled her back to him as he muttered, "Come back here! What's the matter with you?"

She pummeled him with her fists and he grabbed both her wrists with one powerful hand and held her arms above her head as he pinned the rest of her body down with his own. She shrieked with frustration, "Let me go! I hate you! Go find Polly, she'll serve your needs!"

"My needs can't be served by anyone but you, you little witch. Now settle down and listen to me."

She saw his mouth descending to meet hers and tried to turn her head but he was too strong. His lips on hers were hard and cruel, punishing her with a mixture of pain and ecstasy until she stopped fighting. Then they softened, gentled, teasing her into submission.

It was only then that he broke it off and spoke

against the corner of her trembling mouth. "If you'd only opened and read those letters I wrote you, we could both have been saved a lot of anguish. I didn't tell Polly I had a *duty* to take you out, and I did *not* take her to Australia with me, at least not the way you think."

He relaxed his hold on her wrists and she put her arms down as she looked at him, puzzled. "But she said—"

"I know what she said," he murmured grimly, "and afterwards you wouldn't give me a chance to explain." He moved his body off hers and lay beside her, imprisoning her legs with one of his. "Polly wanted me to go to a party with her, but I told her I already had plans for the evening. I didn't even mention you. That little speech about *duty* was simply a performance for your benefit."

A wave of relief surged through her and she relaxed in Matt's arms. Even though she had no reason to, she believed him. But there was still the other matter. Her eyes sought his as she said, "But she went to Australia with you."

Matt shook his head. "No, Anne. She went *at the same time* as I went, not *with* me. Remember, I'd originally planned to go to Australia in November, and at that time she decided she wanted to go too. She talked the television studio into sending her over to do a documentary on the country. Then Rory was killed and I didn't go. She postponed her trip, too, and when she learned that I was going later, she revived her plans. I had nothing to do with it. She didn't ask if I wanted her to come and, believe me, after that little scene at the hotel, I saw as little of her as possible on the trip. Most of the time we weren't even in the same part of the country. I understand she was only there two weeks. Didn't you see the documentary on her news program?"

Anne shook her head, weak with the joy of knowing she'd misjudged Matt. His arms tightened as he pressed her to him and her hands curled into the dark mat of hair on his chest. The musky male smell of him jarred her quivering senses and she moaned softly as he trailed kisses down her throat and cupped the ample swell of her breast with his hand.

She slid her fingers up the rough skin of his chest until they met behind his neck. His voice was husky as he murmured against the hollow of her shoulder, "How I missed you. You've haunted my dreams for so long I can't remember what it's like to have a good night's sleep." He slipped the thin straps of her gown off her shoulders and buried his face between the smooth globes of her breasts. "I've waited so long for you, Anne. I can't wait any longer."

Neither can I, thought Anne, as his exploring hands touched nerve ends and her body responded with searing passion. He lifted her chin with his fingers and this time his kiss was demanding and urgent. Her lips parted to admit his seeking tongue and she arched her body to his. She wanted to give him whatever he wanted, take whatever he would give. She wanted to be awakened to the mysteries of love.

Then she remembered. That's just what Matt was

doing, awakening her. She was innocent, but Matt thought she was his brother's widow. If he took her now he would know she was a virgin and so couldn't possibly be Angela Hawthorne! She couldn't let him go any further without giving away her deception.

She stiffened and pulled her mouth from his as she cried, "No, Matt! Oh, please, I can't."

His eyes opened with surprise, but his hands continued to roam as he muttered, "Stop it, Anne! Don't play the innocent virgin; we've gone too far to stop now. You know how desperately I want you, and you want me too. You don't even try to deny it, so what's the problem? We're full-grown consenting adults, and we're not hurting anybody. We can't possibly sleep down the hall from each other without becoming lovers. You're not going to tease me into marriage the way you did Rory, but you're financially independent now. In a few weeks, when we've had enough of each other, you can have your pick of the wealthy bachelors in and around Denver if you still want to marry money."

His mouth plundered hers angrily, impatient to complete what he had started.

Anne was stunned by his callousness and renewed her struggle to free herself. She had been loving him and all the while he had only been wanting her. She twisted her head and pummeled him with her fists until he angrily pushed her away from him.

She sat up and pulled the sheet around her as he shouted, "What are you trying to do to me? I've had enough of your theatrics!"

She jumped out of bed, dragging the sheet with

her. "Get out of here, Matt!" Her voice was choked with fury at his betrayal. "I'm not going to be your sometime lover. There are plenty of other women who will play that role for you—you don't need me!"

He got up and reached for his slacks, his eyes cold as they raked over her. "You're so right." His tone was as cold as his eyes. "I can't stand women who tease, and you're the worst tease I've ever had the rotten luck to know. I have no intention of standing meekly by while you torment me." He finished fastening his shirt and jammed his feet into his loafers. "Don't worry, Anne, I won't bother you again. You'll have to find someone else to play your little games with."

He picked up his coat and tie and walked quietly out of the room. Anne stood for a long time staring at the closed door and wondered if the human heart really could break.

For the next two weeks Anne lived in a special kind of purgatory, suspended between the heaven of Jim's paternal love and his need of her care, and the hell of Matt and Constance's contempt. It was torture to continue to live in the Hawthornes' home but she couldn't leave, not until Wolf returned. Jim was coming along nicely but he had been dangerously ill and he still needed the assistance he would allow only Anne to give him.

Anne wondered how much longer she could go on this way. Constance was barely civil to her and Matt ignored her entirely, except at dinner, the one time when they were all together with Jim. Then everyone laughed and talked and acted like one big happy

171

family. The pretense was for Jim's sake. He wasn't strong enough yet to deal with the tensions that were tearing Anne apart.

She even wondered if Matt had been lying to her about his relationship with Polly in Australia. If they *had* been estranged, they were certainly back together now. She appeared at the house frequently, but Anne managed to avoid her by staying in her room, pretending to study.

It was Polly, a newswoman trained to be alert to undercurrents in human relationships, who lit the fuse that blasted Anne's own special purgatory wide open. It started with a quarrel between Jim and Polly. Constance had invited Polly to the house to discuss the details of a charity fashion show they were both involved in, and since the planning lasted until dinner time, Constance asked her to stay.

Anne explained that she had a test the following day and would have her dinner in her room while she studied. Jim wouldn't hear of it. "You have to eat, and it doesn't take any longer to eat down here with the rest of us. You can study later."

Anne couldn't refuse without causing a scene. Dinner was a disaster. Even Jim seemed to pick up the tension that settled in the room like a fog, and when Polly suddenly turned her attention from Matt to Anne and asked her how much longer she intended to visit the Hawthornes, Jim snapped, "Anne is not 'visiting'. She lives here and there will be no talk of her leaving!"

Polly's eyebrow tilted but her voice was deferential as she said, "I'm sorry, James. I know you're fond of her, but she's not a child. Angela is a widow in her midtwenties, and I imagine she'll want to resume a normal life again soon."

Jim glared at her. "And just what do you call a 'normal' life? She has everything she could want right here!"

The huge table put too much distance between Anne and Jim for her to reach over and touch him, try to calm him. Matt gave Polly a furious look and grated, "I'd advise you to change the subject, Polly."

Polly took the hint and shortly afterwards Anne excused herself and escaped to her room. But Polly intended to have the last word, as Anne found out a week later.

It was a Saturday morning and Anne, who had been sleeping poorly, overslept once she finally dozed off. She quickly pulled on designer blue jeans and a pale lavender soft terry pullover before parting her hair down the middle and tying it on either side with pieces of lavender yarn. Her creamy young complexion needed no makeup, and she realized, as she glanced in the mirror on the way out of the room, that dressed like that she didn't even look her true age of twenty, let alone Angela's age of twenty-four. It was too late to do anything about it, however, and she bounded down the staircase and into the breakfast room, hoping the food hadn't been cleared away yet.

She stopped when she saw Matt standing at the window with his back to her. He must have heard her because he turned and said, "Come in, Anne, and eat your breakfast before everything gets cold."

She murmured an apology for being late and

poured a glass of orange juice. She spooned steamy fragrant oatmeal into a bowl and poured thick cream over it, then carried her meal to the table and sat down. Matt continued to stand at the window as he said, "Polly called a few minutes ago. She's coming over. She has something to discuss with us and has asked that everyone be present."

Anne swallowed a mouthful of oatmeal and didn't look at Matt. What was Polly up to now? Whatever it was, it undoubtedly meant trouble.

She pressed her hand to her suddenly churning stomach. A few seconds later the sound of the door chimes floated musically through the room. She jumped up, hoping to escape, but Matt was too quick for her. He was beside her in an instant with his hand on her elbow, forcing her to walk along beside him across the house and into the library.

Jim and Constance were already there and Polly had seated herself behind the desk and was taking papers from a briefcase. Anne thought she caught a brief look of triumph in the other woman's eyes, but it was gone so quickly that she couldn't be sure. Anne sank down on the loveseat and was surprised when Matt sat beside her.

Polly's voice was low and controlled as she started to talk. "Please believe me, I'm sorry to be the one to bring you this information, but for some time now I've been uneasy about a situation here in your home. Finally, when it became evident that none of you were aware of the—uh—inconsistencies that were evident to me, I decided to instigate an investigation."

Matt, Constance and Jim turned startled expressions on Polly and Anne sighed. Maybe she had no reason to be scared after all. This certainly didn't sound as if it had anything to do with her. She relaxed against the soft cushions and tried to look interested.

Matt, on the other hand, was tense, and as Polly paused he barked impatiently, "Get to the point, Polly; what are you leading up to?"

Polly flicked him a glance of annoyance, then turned her attention to Jim and Constance. "I suppose you could call this a family matter, but I've known you for so long and been so fond of you all that I feel like a member of the family, so I felt justified in doing everything possible to protect you—"

This time it was Jim who interrupted. "For heaven's sake, girl, get on with it. What do you think you have to protect us from?"

Anne had been paying more attention to the interplay between the other four people in the room than to what was being said, but when Jim spoke, a wave of uneasiness swept over her again. What *was* Polly trying to say?

Polly seemed determined to wring every bit of drama out of the scene and shifted the papers on the desk before she looked up and said, "Several days ago I hired a private firm to investigate Angela."

Both Matt and Jim sat upright and chorused almost in unison, "You what?"

A cold chill shook Anne as Polly smiled like an indulgent mother and answered, "Don't be upset; you'll thank me when you hear what I have to say."

Anne knew what was coming, and, although she

was the target, she felt like a spectator sitting in the audience looking at a play. There was a look of satisfaction on Polly's face as she continued. "This young woman," she nodded toward Anne, "is not Angela Hawthorne, Rory's wife. Her name is Martha Anne Greenfield and she's a runaway who was hitchhiking on the highway in Iowa when Rory and Angela picked her up and gave her a ride."

Constance uttered a startled exclamation and Matt sat rigid with shock next to Anne. Jim was the one who spoke, and his voice was hoarse. "That's enough, Polly! I absolutely forbid you to continue!"

Polly gazed at Jim indulgently. "I know this is upsetting to you, James. But she has been deliberately catering to your weaknesses. She stole her elderly aunt's car in Chicago and ran out on both the sweet old lady who'd devoted her life to raising her and the fiance who adored her. Then, when Rory and Angela were killed, she schemed to convince everybody she was Angela. Naturally none of you suspected; there was no reason to. She's an excellent actress, I'll have to give her that. She meant to seduce Matt, then wait a decent interval before insisting that he marry her. She would have been set for life."

Anne sat rooted to her seat, horrified at the way Polly had twisted the facts to make her seem sinister and uncaring. For a second it was as if everybody was holding their breath.

Then a sharp crack split the air and everyone's attention was jerked toward Jim, who had banged his heavy cane on the small but sturdy table. He planted the cane in front of him and leaned heavily on it with both hands as he faced Polly. The scorn in his voice was scathing as he said, "You're slowing up, Polly; what took you so long? I knew Anne's true identity before she'd been here for more than a few weeks." Anne stared at him, stunned, as he continued. "At first I was puzzled because she was so different from the Angela we'd come to know through letters and phone calls. When she came to me the day after Rory's estate was discussed and refused to accept her share, I knew something was wrong." Anne heard Matt gasp behind her, but Jim continued. "I had her investigated and knew her whole history within a few days."

He held out a beckoning hand to Anne and she walked to him, hypnotized by the power of his forceful personality. He put an arm around her and hugged her to him as she swallowed and tried to speak. It came out a ragged whisper. "Why didn't you tell me? Have me arrested? Send me away?"

He spoke to her, but his voice carried around the room. "Because by then it didn't make any difference to me. I didn't love you because I thought you were my son's wife, little one, I love you because you are my very dear daughter. A daughter any father would cherish. I hoped someday you'd trust me enough to confide in me."

Anne's face was wet with tears as she reached up and kissed Jim on the cheek. "Thank you," she said simply.

Jim patted her cheek, but Constance was by no means as forgiving. Her face was white and pinched and her hands were clutching the arms of her chair as she said, "She's making a fool of you, James; all she wants is your money and prestige."

Anne disengaged herself from Jim's protective hold and wiped her wet face with the back of her hands. Her world had come crashing down around her and the best she could hope for was that nobody would prefer charges against her. Before she left she had to try to make them understand why she had deceived them.

At first her voice was ragged as she said, "Mrs. Hawthorne, it's not the way you think. I had no idea Jim knew who I really am. I don't want your money."

Constance shook her head and sobbed, "Lies! You've been living a lie ever since you came here."

Anne glanced at Matt now standing beside his mother's chair, but his face was unreadable. He might as well have been carved from stone for all the emotion he exhibited. It was as though he were an outsider looking in, a bored spectator waiting for the show to be over so he could leave. She couldn't stand his attitude of indifference and turned again to Constance. "Believe me, I've been only too well aware of that. I never wanted to be Angela, but at first I was afraid of being sent back to Aunt Martha and Clarence and later I was sure you'd send me to jail. I was going to tell you after Rory's funeral, but when I went for a walk and got lost, Matt scolded me and said any shock or emotional upset might kill Jim. I couldn't tell him knowing that!"

Again Constance shook her head. "You can stop

this little charade; I'm not as gullible as my husband!"

For some reason it was desperately important to Anne that Constance and Matt understand her motives. She pleaded, "Please, Mrs. Hawthorne, Matt, let me tell you why I posed as Rory's widow."

Constances's sobs deepened as she buried her face in her hands. Matt walked over to Anne and stood in front of her. He was very close. With just a slight movement of her hand she could have touched him.

She put her hands behind her and stepped back as Matt's eyes sought hers and he spoke in a strained voice. "Go ahead, Anne. Tell us about it."

She started at the beginning and told them of her parents' deaths and her narrow, restricted upbringing by Aunt Martha, of the forced engagement to Clarence and Aunt Martha's threat to report her car stolen if Anne left. She held nothing back as she spoke of her car trouble, the meeting with Rory and Angela and the fiery crash on the Nebraska highway that killed both of them.

It became more difficult as she explained about the mixup in identity and her decision to become Angela. She offered no excuses, only facts, as she told of the difficulty in maintaining her deception, of her growing attachment to Jim, who was willing to be the father she had never had. She was adamant in her assertion that as soon as Wolf came back she would have confessed her deception and left.

As she spoke, she occasionally turned toward Polly, who was slumping behind the desk, her face bleak with astonishment. When Anne finished she turned and walked out of the room. Behind her she heard Jim speak to Polly in a clipped, glacial voice. "You are no longer welcome in my home, Polly. Please gather up your ill-conceived report on my daughter and leave as quickly as possible."

It didn't take Anne long to pack. She took only the few clothes that belonged to her, not to Angela Hawthorne. She took the keys from her purse and put them on her dressing table. She wouldn't need the house key anymore and the car was Jim's, not hers.

She got up and shut her suitcase, the one Matt had bought for her in Nebraska. With a last look around the beautiful room, she reached for the fake fur cape Matt had given her. She picked it up just as a knock sounded on the door. Before she could answer, it opened and Matt strode in.

He ignored her gasp of surprise as he said, "I've been looking for you, Anne; I want to talk to you." His eyes raked over the coat she held and her suitcase beside the bed and he frowned. "Where do you think you're going?"

She stepped back to put more distance between them. She hadn't wanted to see Matt again. It would have been easier if she could have left without having to listen to his scathing indictment of her.

She turned away and said, "Don't worry, I won't abuse your hospitality any longer. If you'll phone for a cab, I'll wait on the porch."

He drew in his breath and she braced herself for the scolding she knew was coming. Instead, he sounded hurt. "You always stiffen and hunch your shoulders as if preparing to ward off a blow when I talk to you. Have I ever hit you, Anne?"

She shook her head, still not looking at him. "No, but you'd be justified this time."

"That's true," he gritted, "but all I was going to do was ask where you'll be staying."

Anne shrugged. "I'll find a place, it's not your worry. Now if you'll please call a cab—"

She reached down to pick up her suitcase, but he beat her to it as he said, "That won't be necessary. I know just the place for you; I'll take you there."

That wasn't what she wanted at all. "No, Matt. I'd rather go alone—"

She was talking to herself; he was already out the door and down the hall with her bag.

As the car sped down the city streets, now devoid of snow, Anne cowered against the door and tried to sound calm as she talked to Matt. "I'm going to continue going to school, so you can find me there if you decide to prosecute."

Matt's hands tightened on the steering wheel. "Good; I'll remember."

She shivered. Well, what had she expected? Just because Jim understood and forgave her didn't mean Matt and Constance would.

She huddled deeper into the corner of her seat and tried again. "I promise not to upset your mother again. I won't attempt to get in touch with Jim."

A muscle twitched at the corner of Matt's mouth as he muttered roughly. "Oh, by all means, desert Dad now that he's kept your secret all this time.

181

Mother and I will enjoy watching him suffer the agony of a broken heart."

Anne sat up, shocked. "Matt!"

He turned the car into the underground garage of a tall building constructed of metal and glass. "Well what on earth do you expect?" He parked the car and got out, leaving her to get out and run after him.

They went up in the elevator. Matt stood fuming as Anne, unable to look at him, watched the floor lights go on and off. What had she said to upset him now? And where was he taking her? She could never afford an apartment here, and he must know that.

The elevator stopped when the lights lit up "Penthouse," and Matt took her arm roughly and propelled her toward a black lacquered door. He unlocked it and escorted Anne inside. She gasped as he guided her through the small entry. The room before her was large and luxuriously furnished with thick carpet, heavy masculine furniture, and two walls of windows that offered a breathtaking view of the rugged, snowcapped mountains. She turned to find a dining room furnished with gleaming mahogany and separated from the compact kitchen beyond by a high bar. It was a bachelor's dream apartment.

Anne was speechless as Matt eyed her somewhat autocratically. "Well, how do you like it? Come on, I'll show you the bedroom and bath."

He took her arm, but she refused to move. "Matt, what do you think you're doing? Why did you bring me here? I couldn't possibly afford anything like this. Besides, the place is obviously already occupied."

Matt grinned. "I know. It belongs to me."

"You!" she shrieked.

Matt explained patiently. "I own the building and keep the penthouse for my own use."

Anne winced. "You mean this is where you bring Polly when you want to—to be alone?" she finished lamely.

His fingers bit into her arm. "Forget Polly!" he shouted. "I mean I want to live here with you."

Anne felt rage build up inside her at the painful thrust of his words. He still thought he could use her to satisfy his lust and then pass her on to one of his wealthy friends. Now that he knew she'd never been his brother's wife he could take her without guilt.

She whirled away from him and her voice was hoarse with outrage as she said, "Just because I was desperate enough to take another woman's identity until I could support myself doesn't mean I'll stoop to what you want of me! I'll starve first!"

She started for the door, but in two long strides he caught her and held her to him in a rib-bruising grip. He was almost as angry as she was. "Oh, no, you don't. You're mine, Anne. I found you in that hospital in Nebraska and brought you home with me. I took care of you, undressed you, put you to bed, combed your hair. We've even slept in each other's arms! You belong to me and I'm not going to let you leave!"

His mouth captured hers before she could turn her face away and she melted under his masterful seduction. His grip relaxed and became a caress as his hands trailed fire down her spine. She hated herself for being such a fool, but she couldn't help it. She loved him and there was nothing she could do about it. He slipped the cape from her shoulders and let it fall to the floor as his lips moved down to the sensitive hollows of her throat and his hand cupped her breast. She trembled with the hunger he was arousing in her. If she didn't escape quickly she'd give herself to him and become an object for him to enjoy and then toss away when he became bored.

She put the palms of her hands against his chest and pushed herself away as he raised his head and looked at her, surprised. She bit her quivering lip and said, "Please let me go, Matt. I won't live here as your mistress."

He cocked an eyebrow and eyed her curiously. "My mistress! Is that what you thought? I don't want a mistress, Anne, I want a wife. Sweetheart, I'm asking you to marry me!"

She swayed as dizziness threatened to overcome her and Matt's arms tightened as he once more molded her to him. She wished she could just accept what he'd said and leave it at that, but she couldn't. She had to know.

"Why, Matt?" Her voice was muffled in his chest. "Why do you want to marry me? If it's just so you can take me to bed, it won't be worth it to you. I'm too inexperienced. I've never—never slept with a man."

Matt chuckled. "Yes, you have. You've slept with me."

She could feel the warm flush of embarrassment. "That's different. You know what I mean."

He rubbed his cheek in her blonde curls. "I know what you mean, my love, but I can't believe you're so naive. Come sit down and I'll tell you why I want to marry you."

He removed his coat and tie and they curled up together on the soft cushions of the massive modular sofa. He lifted her face and kissed her again with a tenderness that quickly turned to passion and he groaned as he broke off. "You really don't know how much I love you, do you? I know now I fell in love with you the first time I saw you in that hospital bed. You looked like a bruised and battered child lying there so still. I wanted to hold you, protect you.

"As I got to know you, you were so different from the Angela I had learned to dislike through phone calls and letters. I didn't even realize what was happening to me until that night we shared a motel room in Sterling. I thought nothing of it when I signed for the room, but by the time I'd undressed you and tucked you into bed I knew I wanted you for myself."

Anne wondered if it was possible to contain so much happiness or if she would burst into little pieces. She snuggled closer into Matt's arms and he nuzzled her neck as he continued. "Remember, honey, I thought you were Angela. I knew what a little tramp she was, how she'd tricked my brother into marrying her, then let him know she'd only wanted him for his money. I was prepared to make her pay for what she'd done to Rory, and I was appalled to find that I'd fallen hopelessly in love with her—*you*. It's clear now that I hated Angela and loved Anne and it made my life a lonely, frustrating torment, because I didn't know they were two different people!"

Anne held him and stroked his hair as she murmured, "I'm sorry, darling."

He nibbled her earlobe and growled, "I should hope so! Why didn't you tell me, Anne? You knew how I felt. That night after Rory's funeral when I came to you, I couldn't control my need for you and I lashed out with the cruelest accusation I could find. When I denounced you for either lying about being pregnant or getting rid of Rory's baby, why didn't you tell me the truth? Why have you tormented me almost beyond endurance?"

The anguish in his voice brought tears to Anne's eyes, and she rained kisses over his face as she murmured, "I didn't! Oh, Matt, I swear I didn't do it intentionally. I thought you just wanted me like a new toy, to use and then discard when you found someone new." He shook his head in denial, but she hurried on. "You even told me that's the way you wanted it that morning after . . . after . . ." Her voice broke and she looked pleadingly at him.

He moaned and clutched her tighter. "Oh, Anne, when you bring a man to the brink of fulfillment and then push him away, there's no telling what he might say. I was in agony!"

"I know, darling, so was I, but I knew if I let you make love to me you'd know it was my first time and that I couldn't have been Rory's wife. I was afraid you'd put me in jail, or, worse, that the shock of the whole thing would be too much for Jim. He was still so sick." She thought of something. "Your mother will never accept me as your wife. She hates me. She'd probably like you to marry Polly."

He shrugged. "Mother's approval would be nice, but we don't need it to be happy, and there was never any chance of my marrying Polly. She was a charming companion, but not the woman I'd want for the mother of my children. I only started taking her out again after I got back from Australia to make you jealous. There hasn't been anything—physical— between us since I got saddled with you." He grinned. "You've been haunting my bed, you little gremlin."

She giggled and her teeth teased his lower lip. He groaned softly and pulled her against his hard male body. She felt the tremor that shook him as his mouth covered hers, urgent in its hunger. She moaned softly with frustration as he lifted his head and looked deep into her eyes. "I'm glad you weren't my brother's wife, Anne. It would have torn me apart to know that he'd had you first, but I'd have married you just the same. I couldn't have helped myself. I've known for a long time now that I had to have you, but I couldn't tell you how much I loved you or ask you to be my wife until I got my jealousy under control. You'll never know how re-lieved I was when Polly announced that you weren't Angela."

As he spoke, he loosened the buttons at the back of her blouse, the same blouse he had bought for her in Nebraska. His lips sought hers as he pulled it forward and helped her out of it. His eyes gleamed with desire at the sight of her soft, free breasts and he caressed them lightly, reverently.

With trembling hands she unbuttoned his shirt and ran her fingertips through the dark mat of hair on his chest until they became entangled in it. He trailed fiery kisses down her throat and into the cleavage between her tantalizingly scented breasts.

Anne knew she wouldn't stop him this time, couldn't stop him, but he apparently wasn't prey to the same emotions. With a shudder, he pushed her none too gently away and sat up, raking his trembling fingers through his dark hair. She pulled herself up, puzzled, and pleaded, "Matt, what's the matter? Did I do something wrong?"

He handed her her blouse and stood up as he buttoned his shirt. "My self-control is practically nonexistent where you're concerned, but I'm not in the habit of deflowering young maidens before the marriage vows have been spoken." He turned and looked at her tenderly as he said, "Go in the bedroom and straighten yourself up a bit. You look like you've been ravaged."

She stretched up and kissed him. "I think I have been."

His hands tightened around her upper arms as he held her away from him. "Not quite, but you will be if you don't put some distance between us. Now run along and lock the bedroom door behind you while I arrange for a marriage license. If we don't get those vows said before nightfall, all my good intentions will go up in smoke. I don't intend to spend another night in bed without you, and this time don't expect to sleep."

He turned to the phone and she retreated to the bedroom, humming the wedding march in a lilting, soprano voice.

Silhouette Romance

ROMANCE THE WAY
IT USED TO BE...
AND COULD BE AGAIN

Contemporary romances for today's women.

Each month, six very special love stories will be yours

from SILHOUETTE.

Look for them wherever books are sold

or order now from the coupon below.

$1.50 each

___# 1 PAYMENT IN FULL Hampson	___#25 SHADOW OF LOVE Stanford
___# 2 SHADOW AND SUN Carroll	___#26 INNOCENT FIRE Hastings
___# 3 AFFAIRS OF THE HEART Powers	___#27 THE DAWN STEALS SOFTLY Hampson
___# 4 STORMY MASQUERADE Hampson	___#28 MAN OF THE OUTBACK Hampson
___# 5 PATH OF DESIRE Goforth	___#29 RAIN LADY Wildman
___# 6 GOLDEN TIDE Stanford	___#30 RETURN ENGAGEMENT Dixon
___# 7 MIDSUMMER BRIDE Lewis	___#31 TEMPORARY BRIDE Halldorson
___# 8 CAPTIVE HEART Beckman	___#32 GOLDEN LASSO Michaels
___# 9 WHERE MOUNTAINS WAIT Wilson	___#33 A DIFFERENT DREAM Vitek
___#10 BRIDGE OF LOVE Caine	___#34 THE SPANISH HOUSE John
___#11 AWAKEN THE HEART Vernon	___#35 STORM'S END Stanford
___#12 UNREASONABLE SUMMER Browning	___#36 BRIDAL TRAP McKay
___#13 PLAYING FOR KEEPS Hastings	___#37 THE BEACHCOMBER Beckman
___#14 RED, RED ROSE Oliver	___#38 TUMBLED WALL Browning
___#15 SEA GYPSY Michaels	___#39 PARADISE ISLAND Sinclair
___#16 SECOND TOMORROW Hampson	___#40 WHERE EAGLES NEST Hampson
___#17 TORMENTING FLAME John	___#41 THE SANDS OF TIME Owen
___#18 THE LION'S SHADOW Hunter	___#42 DESIGN FOR LOVE Powers
___#19 THE HEART NEVER FORGETS Thornton	___#43 SURRENDER IN PARADISE Robb
___#20 ISLAND DESTINY Fulford	___#44 DESERT FIRE Hastings
___#21 SPRING FIRES Richards	___#45 TOO SWIFT THE MORNING Carroll
___#22 MEXICAN NIGHTS Stephens	___#46 NO TRESPASSING Stanford
___#23 BEWITCHING GRACE Edwards	___#47 SHOWERS OF SUNLIGHT Vitek
___#24 SUMMER STORM Healy	___#48 A RACE FOR LOVE Wildman

Silhouette Romance

___ #49 DANCER IN THE SHADOWS Wisdom
___ #50 DUSKY ROSE Scott
___ #51 BRIDE OF THE SUN Hunter
___ #52 MAN WITHOUT A HEART Hampson
___ #53 CHANCE TOMORROW Browning
___ #54 LOUISIANA LADY Beckman
___ #55 WINTER'S HEART Ladame
___ #56 RISING STAR Trent
___ #57 TO TRUST TOMORROW John
___ #58 LONG WINTER'S NIGHT Stanford
___ #59 KISSED BY MOONLIGHT Vernon
___ #60 GREEN PARADISE Hill
___ #61 WHISPER MY NAME Michaels
___ #62 STAND-IN BRIDE Halston
___ #63 SNOWFLAKES IN THE SUN Brent
___ #64 SHADOW OF APOLLO Hampson
___ #65 A TOUCH OF MAGIC Hunter

___ #66 PROMISES FROM THE PAST Vitek
___ #67 ISLAND CONQUEST Hastings
___ #68 THE MARRIAGE BARGAIN Scott
___ #69 WEST OF THE MOON St. George
___ #70 MADE FOR EACH OTHER Afton Bonds
___ #71 A SECOND CHANCE ON LOVE Ripy
___ #72 ANGRY LOVER Beckman
___ #73 WREN OF PARADISE Browning
___ #74 WINTER DREAMS Trent
___ #75 DIVIDE THE WIND Carroll
___ #76 BURNING MEMORIES Hardy
___ #77 SECRET MARRIAGE Cork
___ #78 DOUBLE OR NOTHING Oliver
___ #79 TO START AGAIN Halldorson
___ #80 WONDER AND WILD DESIRE Stephens
___ #81 IRISH THOROUGHBRED Roberts

- -

SILHOUETTE BOOKS, Department SB/1
1230 Avenue of the Americas
New York, NY 10020

Please send me the books I have checked above. I am enclosing
$_____ (please add 50¢ to cover postage and handling. NYS and
NYC residents please add appropriate sales tax). Send check or
money order—no cash or C.O.D.'s please. Allow six weeks for delivery.

NAME_____

ADDRESS_____

CITY_____STATE/ZIP_____